THE MAGNITUDE AND ECONOMIC

IMPACT OF GENERAL AVIATION

1968 – 1980

A Report Prepared for the

General Aviation Manufacturers' Association (GAMA)

By R. Dixon Speas Associates

AERO HOUSE
Manhasset, New York

PREFACE

In March, 1968, a dozen of the world's leading manufacturers of General Aviation aircraft and engines commissioned R. Dixon Speas Associates of Manhasset, New York, to undertake a comprehensive study of "The Magnitude and Economic Impact of General Aviation" in the United States. Today, these sponsoring companies form the nucleus of the General Aviation Manufacturers Association, Inc. (GAMA) — founded January 1, 1970. (At the time the study was initiated, the underwriting firms comprised the Utility Airplane Council of the Aerospace Industries Association of America, Inc.)

GAMA is an independent trade organization dedicated to fostering and advancing the general welfare, safety, interests and activities of all facets of General Aviation. It seeks to develop General Aviation's relationships with other segments of the aviation community, other modes of transportation, and in so doing, also seeks to promote the public welfare. At the time of its founding, GAMA's membership base was broadened to include, in addition to manufacturers of aircraft and powerplants, makers of avionics, components and materials used in the construction and operation of General Aviation aircraft.

The principal objective of the original study by Speas Associates was to produce data and forecasts whch would assist in the formulation of policy and for planning within an area of aviation which, despite its size, remains relatively unknown.

In July, 1969, a year after delivery of the first report, Speas Associates was requested to update and further quantify some of the basic information included in the earlier study. The present publication integrates in a single volume the findings of the 1968 and 1969 reports, covering the development of General Aviation between 1968 and 1980. This book seeks to assist industry and government in the achievement of the goal of a dynamic and integrated transportation structure, in which the role to be played by General Aviation will be clearly recognized and planned for. Particular attention has been given to the requirements of those forecasts which relate to technological achievements as correlated with market demands.

Insofar as the forecasts undertaken are demand forecasts, they are based on the premise that there will be no important new constraints on growth in this sector. This was an assumption stipulated by the sponsors to provide proper perspective for the planning use of the studies. The results thus emphasize the urgent requirement to upgrade General Aviation facilities to accommodate this forecast growth. Improvements in the nation's air traffic control systems and airport facilities to accommodate the projected growth are technologically attainable. There is a need, however, for a comprehensive national program, if the requisite airports, air traffic flow systems, and other related facilities are to be forthcoming.

It now seems that these facilities are likely to be provided. As this book goes to press, it appears that the United States Congress will approve the "Airport and Airways Development Act of 1969." This will make available substantial funds during the 1970s to enlarge and improve the efficiency, capacity and safety of the national aviation system.

The studies look at the future of General Aviation from two points of view which are implicit in the title. On the one hand, an attempt has been made to determine the actual magnitude of the future development of this segment of the aviation industry, and on the other, an evaluation has been made of the economic impact of this growth.

Determining the magnitude of future development involved consideration of the actual number of active aircraft, the number of flying hours and movements, and the number of airmen and user profiles. Forecasts were derived not only for the national values but also by state and Standard Metropolitan Statistical Area.

In order to accomplish this first task, Speas Associates undertook an exhaustive examination of existing industry data. Variances were found in the historical material examined, but these differences did not have a significant influence upon the results of the study. The lack of certain basic data necessitated an extensive research and data development effort, which included the wide use of computer programming. As a result of this effort, a substantial amount of new basic data has been developed for past and future values.

The economic impact of the report determined General Aviation's contribution to the national economy by evaluating such factors as the value of production and sales of aircraft and avionics, the used aircraft market, user costs, investment spending by manufacturers, dealers and operators, and government outlays. In this way, an estimate of the direct contribution to the economy was measured; no attempt was made to quantify the indirect impact.

The information presented is to be used primarily by national and local government bodies and other elements of the aviation community in their planning for transportation facilities and to illustrate the economic benefits which accrue from general aviation.

In accomplishing the objectives of this study, as outlined previously, Speas Associates worked directly with the founding-member companies of GAMA and the organization's professional staff. Whereas Speas Associates exercised full responsibility for the analysis and research results, the GAMA committees and staff were helpful in establishing the scope and in reviewing the progress of work involved.

Rand McNally and Company cooperated in the analysis of demographic considerations, and Planning Research Corporation actively assisted in determining the economic impact.

The General Aviation manufacturing companies who jointly supported the funding and assisted in accomplishment of the research were:

> Avco Corporation
>   Lycoming Division (Williamsport Operations)
>
> Beech Aircraft Corporation
>
> Cessna Aircraft Company

Continental Motors Corporation

The Garrett Corporation

General Electric Company
  Aircraft Engine Group (Commercial Engine Division)

Grumman Aircraft Engineering Corporation

Lear Jet Industries, Inc.

Lockheed-Georgia Company

North American Rockwell Corporation
  General Aviation Division

Piper Aircraft Corporation

United Aircraft Corporation

Publication of this volume by R. Dixon Speas Associates is with the express permission of the above-listed firms.

Manhasset, New York
February, 1970

CONTENTS

Chapter Seven

Chapter Eight

FIGURE INDEX

CHAPTER ONE

GENERAL AVIATION
AIRCRAFT FLEET POPULATION

A detailed analysis of the General Aviation fleet population was undertaken for two principal reasons:

- First, to ascertain, within the constraints of this study, the current size of the General Aviation active fleet population, based upon a realistic and operational definition of the word "active". The active fleet size was determined as of December 31, for the two years 1967 and 1968.

- Second, following from the preceding objective, to provide the most objective data base from which to forecast the future General Aviation aircraft population and its economic impact for the years 1975 and 1980.

This evaluation further provides the basis for determining the numbers of the various categories of aircraft types, which, taken together, constitute the overall General Aviation fleet. The overall fleet population also provides the framework within which the geographical distribution of aircraft, airmen, flying hours and movements are undertaken.

One of the primary objectives of this study was to define the implications of the continued growth of general aviation for long-term policy formulation. In consequence, the forecast values are for medium to long term horizon dates, 1975 and 1980, rather than for the short term.

Summary

Analysis by SPEAS shows that as of December 31, 1968, there were 130,000 active General Aviation aircraft in the U.S. fleet, an increase of slightly more than 6 percent over the previous year's figure of 122,200 aircraft. It is forecast that the active fleet will further increase by 47.7 percent by 1975, to give a total fleet population of 192,000. By 1980 the General Aviation fleet active in the United States is expected to number 260,000 aircraft, up 100 percent from the 1968 figure and 35.4 percent from the 1975 figure. FooT Note

The SPEAS forecast of active aircraft in 1980 is approximately 17 percent higher than the implied value of 223,000 eligible aircraft in the most recent Federal Aviation Administration forecast. An important part of the difference is attributable to the different definitions, which are discussed in Section 2 of this chapter, of "active" aircraft as used here and "eligible" aircraft as determined by the FAA. Figure 1 represents a comparison of the two forecasts.

It is significant that, apart from the FAA forecast, there have only been a limited number of cursory forecasts available to the public covering this very large and important segment of the aviation industry. It is this prior lack of public information and associated study which permits characterizing the present study as "breaking new ground." Sponsorship of this project by the General Aviation Manufacturers' Association has enabled the devotion of considerable analytical effort to an area of aviation which, heretofore, has not received adequate research, considering the size of the General Aviation sector and its impact on the U.S. air transportation system. Much of the work described in this book covers new, applied research information and new approaches to analyzing the general aviation industry.

1. Analysis of Fleet Forecast Made by Others

It is somewhat incongruous, considering the size of the General Aviation industry and the

1

2

Figure 1

FORECASTS OF GENERAL AVIATION ACTIVE AIRCRAFT

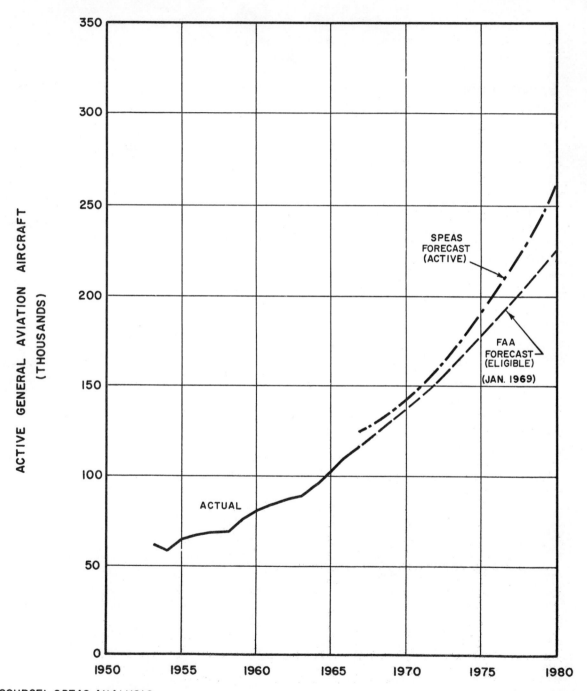

SOURCE: SPEAS ANALYSIS
FAA, AVIATION FORECASTS 1968-1980

number of people interested in it, to find that there are apparently very few in-depth studies of the industry. At the inception of this project, a thorough search was undertaken of the major sources of aviation information in the United States. Extensive personal interviews and telephone contacts were employed to ensure that important forecast information was secured in the course of this investigation. The net result of these efforts was the conclusion that only two important sources of forecast information exist concerning General Aviation — the FAA and the manufacturers of General Aviation aircraft.

The Federal Aviation Administration has, for many years, produced forecasts of the General Aviation fleet and in 1965 undertook what was then the most thoroughly researched forecast. The major manufacturers of General Aviation aircraft have also completed work in the forecasting area. In most cases, the manufacturers' work has been in their own specific fields of particular or immediate interest; relatively little forecasting has been completed regarding the complete General Aviation spectrum. A few remaining forecasts available to the public can, in almost all cases, be traced back to work done by the FAA or are "guesstimates" made by enlightened people within the industry.

a) *The FAA Forecast*

The basic FAA forecast of General Aviation aircraft was analyzed to determine the methodology employed and its possible application in this study. Discussions with members of the FAA along with detailed evaluations of such studies as "General Aviation: A Study and Forecast of the Fleet and Its Use in 1975", "Aviation Forecasts Fiscal Years 1968-1979", "The National Airport Plan, 1968-1972", and numerous other FAA publications give substance to the following findings:

First, the FAA's forecast of the period 1968 to 1979 shows a net addition to the fleet of 8-9,000 units annually, throughout the forecast period. This results in a forecast for fiscal year 1980 of 223,000 general aviation aircraft in the U.S. fleet.

Second, this forecast is reportedly based on "past trends", although it is more than a mere extrapolation. The FAA conducted several exercises in an attempt to establish basic correlations with the major economic indicators — particularly Gross National Product — but these proved unsuccessful.

Third, the average annual compound growth rate of the FAA 1968-1979 forecast for the General Aviation fleet is 5.5%. This rate is the same as the U. S. GNP growth rate (in current dollars) for the 1954-1965 time period, and suggests that at some point in the background development of the forecast, the FAA recognized an association with GNP to obtain the 1979 fleet population.

Fourth, the mechanics of the FAA forecast are also related to civil aircraft production projections. The FAA forecasts of production, exports and retirement (attrition) rates were based upon historical trends, interviews with manufacturers, and judgment. It was concluded that considerable original research was required to substantiate the FAA's forecast values — and this research would be better applied in pursuing a completely independent approach. Consequently, no use of the FAA's forecast was made in this study.

b) *General Aviation Manufacturers' Forecasts*

As part of the preliminary research phase of this study, representatives of the major manufacturers were interviewed to collect projections of the future fleet size. In all but one case, the manufacturers had estimates of annual production, but not estimates of the size of the overall fleet. These forecasts were based almost exclusively on the manufacturer's experience, rather than upon theoretical or statistical analyses. This finding did not reduce the validity of the forecasts, since the manufacturers are better qualified than most to make judgments as to the future of General Aviation — but it once again indicated the need in this study for an independent methodology to forecast the active fleet.

c) *Other Forecasts*

All of the other forecasts which were reviewed (after being adjusted for differences in base data and forecast years) fell between the FAA and the manufacturers' projections. In most cases, the forecast methodology was not apparent from the source and, therefore, they were of no assistance in suggesting the best methodology to employ in developing reliable forecasting techniques.

It was concluded from the investigations in this field that they could not be used or adapted for the present study. GAMA sponsorship of this study provided the opportunity to contribute considerable new information for this segment of the aviation industry.

2. *Determination of the Current Size of the "Active" Fleet*

Despite the vast amount of information published by the federal government and other sources, it is difficult to determine accurately the actual size of the General Aviation aircraft fleet, especially that part of the fleet which is "actively" engaged in flying. The first difficulty encountered is one of definition — that is, of defining the meaning of the words "eligible" and "active" as applied to General Aviation aircraft. The FAA, in its reports, frequently uses the term "eligible aircraft", which is a legal definition of the status of an aircraft according to whether or not it has been officially inspected within a specified period of time. This term in several instances does not coincide with the literal definition of "active aircraft", even though the two terms are often used interchangeably.

The distinction arises primarily in three situations. First, a General Aviation aircraft is considered ineligible by the FAA in its fleet tabulations if it is under a so-called "continuous maintenance program" (as most of the turbojet aircraft are), and not therefore subject to the annual inspections whose reports are the basis of indicated eligibility. Second, in handling the obviously large volume of records (one for each registered aircraft), some of the annual

inspection reports are delayed or mis-routed, which causes a legally eligible aircraft to be tabulated by the FAA as ineligible.

Lastly, there are numerous aircraft whose eligibility lapses for one reason or another — usually because the aircraft is not inspected and certified airworthy — but this lapse may be only for a relatively short period of time. In all of these cases, however, the aircraft are active in the sense that they occupy airport space, use aviation facilities and are being, or soon will be, flown. These aircraft provide a service and place a demand on the available supply of aviation facilities and services in spite of their "ineligible" classification. It is therefore considered more meaningful, for the purposes of this study, to include these three categories of ineligible aircraft as active aircraft.

In previous years, the FAA has reported the fleet size at the end of each year on the basis of recorded eligibility and has not made any adjustments to account for the situations discussed above. At the time that work on this study was begun, in July 1968, the latest available figures published by the FAA were for the year ending December 31, 1966. The eligible fleet size at that time was reported as 104,706 aircraft.[4] Although comparable figures for 1967 had not as yet been made public, the FAA informally indicated that the eligible fleet population for that year was of the order of 114,397.[5] Consideration of the manufacturers' domestic sales reports and probable attrition rates tended to confirm this figure.

One of the reasons for which the FAA had not at that time published a population figure for 1967, is that the method employed in tabulating fleet size was being changed. This change resulted from cooperation with an industry group working with the FAA to produce more meaningful information on General Aviation activities. This new derivation was completed

[4]This figure was a compilation of all aircraft which were carried on the record as having been inspected during the previous 13 months. The addition of the extra month was made by the FAA in an effort to partially overcome the problem of records arriving late at the record center in Oklahoma City.

[5]The 1968 edition of the "FAA Statistical Handbook of Aviation" shows a final figure of 114,186 aircraft.

for the year-end 1967, and the result showed that 114,186 aircraft were eligible according to the FAA definition. The new technique allows three months, January, February, and March, to elapse before tabulating the eligible aircraft on record for the 12-month period ending December 31, 1967. This improved methodology allows the updating and tabulation of aircraft records, even though they are processed as late as three months after the required inspection due date.

This latest system still does not account, however, for those aircraft for which the paperwork may have been misrouted and which never gets into the record. Nor does it recognize those aircraft for which only a temporary lapse in eligibility is experienced, or which are on "continuous maintenance."

In order to accommodate these three requirements and to arrive at a full definition of the term "active" aircraft, the 114,400 value was increased as follows:

- 300 aircraft were added for aircraft on continuous maintenance programs.
- 1200 aircraft were added to account for the inspections not recorded.[6]
- 300 aircraft subject to paperwork delay in excess of three months.
- 6000 aircraft experiencing short-term ineligibility and re-entering service within six months.

Figure 2 further explains the foregoing categories and values. The short ineligibility figure of 6000 aircraft was developed from a special analysis of the FAA's Master Aircraft Register computer tapes. Two successive months' data were used to determine the number of aircraft which, although classified by FAA inspection rules as

[6]SPEAS conducted a special direct mail survey of aircraft owners listed by the FAA as having aircraft which did not have current inspection records to determine this estimated number.

Figure 2

DEVELOPMENT OF ACTIVE FLEET
NUMBER OF ACTIVE GENERAL AVIATION AIRCRAFT
AS OF DECEMBER 31, 1967

Fleet of Eligible General Aviation Aircraft
(As of December 31, 1967, per FAA Records as Processed
March 31, 1968)..114,400
Other Active Aircraft
Continuous Maintenance 300
It is assumed that of 6,392 multi-engine aircraft which were ineligible as of 2/29/68 per FAA records, the indicated quantity were on continuous maintenance. Of this total, 5,974 were reciprocating, 190 were turboprop, and 228 were turbojet.
Inspections Not Recorded 1,200
This quantity is based on the results of a direct mail survey to owners of ineligible aircraft.
Paperwork Lag in Excess of Three Months......................... 300
Short Ineligibility Span 6,000
  Aircraft Out for 1 Month..1,900
  Aircraft Out for 2 Months..1,200
  Aircraft Out for 3 Months... 900
  Aircraft Out for 4-6 Months 2,000
                                                                          6,000
These last two quantities are based on a data processing analysis of the records of aircraft which were indicated by the FAA as being ineligible at February 29, 1968 and eligible again at March 31, 1968.
TOTAL ACTIVE AIRCRAFT...122,200

Source: SPEAS Analysis and Development

being ineligible, nevertheless re-entered the active fleet during the intervening month's period. This special tabulation showed that for the period between February 29 and March 31 of 1968, the following approximate number of aircraft re-entered service:

Number of Aircraft	Ineligibility Period
1,900	1 month
600	2 months
300	3 months
400	4-6 months

It is considered logical and proper that six months or less of ineligibility time qualifies an aircraft to be considered part of the active fleet. The above findings cannot be applied directly as the active fleet adjustment because, those aircraft which had been ineligible for only two months and which re-entered the fleet had a like number of aircraft one month behind them. The total number of aircraft, therefore, considered as ineligible with a lapse of two months was 1200.

Similarly, the rest of the findings have to be expanded to reflect other aircraft still considered ineligible, which satisfy the definition of active aircraft. The total of all such aircraft is 6,000 and this value must be added to develop the estimate for the active fleet. As of December 31, 1967, therefore, there were in the United States 122,200 active general aviation aircraft. This is approximately 6.8 percent more than the FAA reported informally. By applying this same adjustment factor to the FAA eligible fleet figure for 1968, it was ascertained that the total General Aviation active fleet, at year end 1968, stood at 130,000 aircraft.

3. The SPEAS Forecast
a) Background Development

The simplicity of the technique ultimately adopted by SPEAS to produce its forecast of the total active General Aviation fleet belies the large amount of effort expended in pursuing many other approaches. The main thrust of this discussion is to describe the actual forecasting technique adopted and also the approaches which were explored but rejected for one reason or another. The following discussion presents the SPEAS forecast and some of its development background in order to demonstrate the credibility of the work and to provide insight as to methodology.

The basic philosophy of the approach was to develop as simple a methodology as possible, consistent with accepted statistical criteria and common sense. Consequently, the initial efforts explored time series analyses using the total eligible fleet, as reported by the FAA, for base data. Although a simple time series analysis showed a reasonable measure of correlation, it was apparent that a more detailed investigation of the factors directly governing the growth of the number of eligible aircraft was called for.

As a second approach, attempts were made to establish linear correlations between various economic indicators, General Aviation aircraft population, and time. These comparisons considered principally the relationships between the growth of the fleet and: GNP, disposable personal income, U.S. population, and expenditures on transportation. These exercises revealed no satisfactory correlations. Next, these same economic indicators were compared to the growth in General Aviation flight hours, but again no simple correlation resulted which could be used for forecasting purposes.

As a consequence of these findings, it was decided to separate the General Aviation activity indicators into the various components reflecting type of aircraft use. A simple division into pleasure flying and other flying (principally business oriented) was first used to test this approach. Against pleasure flying (in hours), disposable personal income was plotted, since this is normally the best indicator of discretionary spending in the consumer sector of the economy. No correlation was found to exist, even when other consumer indicators were tried. Against business flying, several indicators of the growth of the overall economy ∙ and several indicators related specifically to business activity were matched; these produced a

Figure 3

COMPARISON OF DOMESTIC AIRLINE AIRCRAFT AND PASSENGER MILES WITH GENERAL AVIATION BUSINESS MILES FLOWN

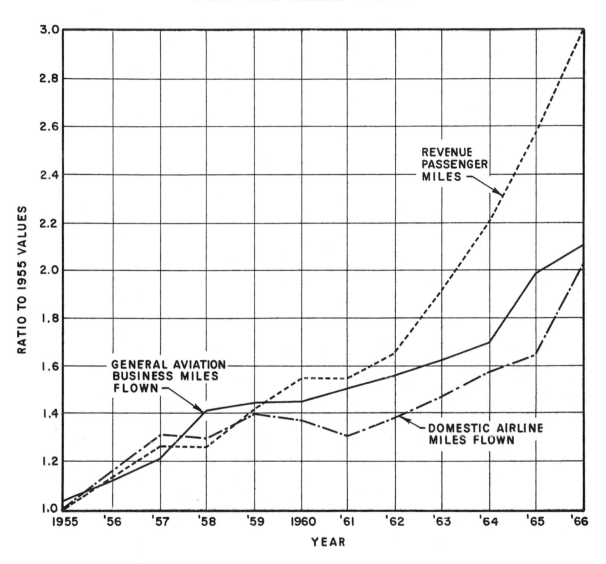

NOTE: VERTICAL SCALE STARTS AT 600 MILLION TO VISULIZE DIFFERENTIALS
SOURCE: FAA STATISTICAL HANDBOOK OF AVIATION ATA 1967 FACTS AND FIGURES

Figure 4

PERCENTAGE GROWTH RATE OF ELIGIBLE GENERAL AVIATION AIRCRAFT

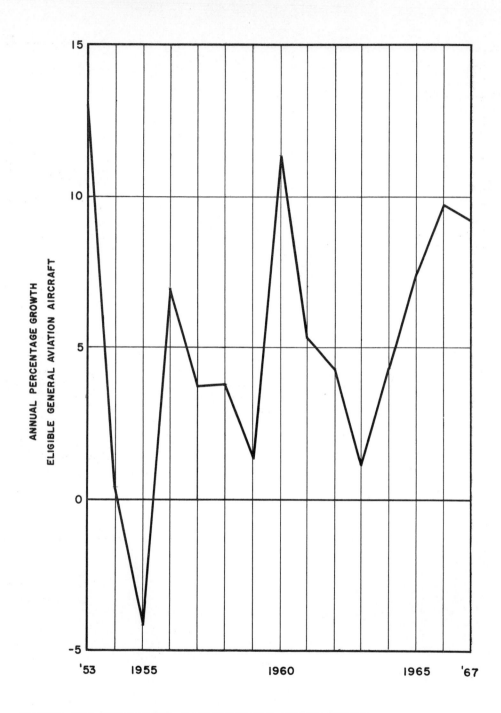

SOURCE: FAA STATISTICAL HANDBOOK FOR YEARS SHOWN.

modest degree of correlation between hours flown and the measures of performance of the overall economy. Domestic airline passenger and aircraft miles were then plotted against General Aviation aircraft miles flown for business reasons; this yielded good mathematical correlation, but still did not satisfactorily explain the past or future growth of General Aviation.

Multiple correlation studies were also undertaken. The added sophistication of this approach is accompanied by an increase in the complexity and difficulty of application. The basic assumption underlying forecasting by means of multivariate regression analysis is that there exists a set of predictable forces (called independent variables) which determine and/or explain the emergence and behaviour of a certain phenomenon (called the dependent variable), and will continue to do so in the future.

In the case of General Aviation, so little is known quantitatively about the factors which influence this activity (and what mathematical expression best explains the relationship between these factors and the activity), that the problem of applying the technique becomes a hit or miss development, refined only by common sense, experience, and general economic theory.

It is convenient, for example, to think in terms of the fleet as representing demand for a service (air transportation), the components of which yield a clue to the economic function governing this demand. The most apparent components are:

a) The demand for business travel, including the various so-called utility applications.

b) The demand for personal travel, if only for the purpose of circling an airport to acquire experience in flying techniques.

These two components help determine the factors which influence the level of the total demand. In accordance with economic theory, an equation representing total demand for General Aviation should contain variables which define business activity and personal consumption behaviour. However, having accepted this assumption, it is difficult to classify beforehand the specific nature of the function or equation which explains the relationship between the dependent and independent variables.

A total of 33 separate regression analyses, each building on the knowledge gained from the previous one, were developed to arrive at an acceptable equation. The list of independent variables considered were selected for their applicability according to their known relationship with business activity and/or personal consumpton behaviour. They were also selected on the basis of the availability and confidence in the forecasts for the factors.

The following is a list of the major factors selected for the analysis:
- Gross National Product.
- U.S. Population.
- Disposable Personal Income.
- Population With a College Education.
- Households With Annual Income Over $10,000.
- Automobile Registrations.
- Expenditures on Plant and Equipment.
- Employment in Manufacturing.
- Commercial Airline Passengers in Scheduled Service.

Each of these variables was correlated with the number of planes in the active fleet (measuring separately each independent variable against the dependent variable in a random sequence of observations; that is, without introducing the time variable at all). All demonstrated coefficients of correlation above .900 and one, Gross National Product, produced a coefficient of .989.[6]

One of the best equations of multiple correlation discovered used the following independent variables:

X_1 = Gross National Product.
X_2 = Disposable Personal Income.
X_3 = Percent of the Population with a College Education.

The calculation of the coefficients and the constant, using data for the 14-year period

[6]Perfect correlation yields a value of 1.000.

1953-1967, yielded the following equation:

$$Y = 20.8 + .18X_1 - .22X_2 + 2.94X_3$$

where GNP and DPI are expressed in billions and Education is in percent. The coefficient of correlation determined for this equation was .991, which is a very good fit. The application of the equation and the observed values of X_1, X_2, and X_3 for 1966 yields a computed value for Y of 105,400 eligible aircraft, whereas the actual total was 104,700. Similar small differences (residuals) can be noted for the other observations.

b) *Final SPEAS Forecast Model*

Concurrently, a simple linear equation relating the individual independent variables to the eligible fleet was also studied. Through several transformations (involving first differences, and logs) and other data manipulations, it was found that GNP was, in fact, the best predictor of the fleet.

The equation ultimately developed and adopted for SPEAS' forecast of the General Aviation fleet contains the important refinement of "time lag". It was found that the best correlation resulted when a one-year time lag was introduced between measuring the GNP and measuring the fleet size. That is, the 1953 GNP best explains the 1954 fleet (and not the 1953 fleet) and so on, for all of the 15 observations. This circumstance has several useful implications outside the scope of this study. The value of this finding for marketing purposes is obvious and suggests the possible benefits to be realized through additional research in this area.[7] For national facilities planners, it also means that they have the short run capability to predict with reasonable accuracy one year ahead, merely by following the progress of the general economy. An additional refinement which was incorporated in the model was the finding that the use of GNP in current dollars yielded significantly better results than using constant dollars.

[7]A quarterly analysis might prove most useful for this purpose; however, quarterly fleet data would have to be generated before such an analysis can be made. FAA does not report quarterly fleet statistics.

The calculation of the constant and coefficient are as follows:

$$Y = 7.14 + .142X$$

The value of the GNP (X in the equation) is expressed in billions of current dollars and the resulting estimate of the fleet (Y in the equation), is in thousands of eligible aircraft.

SPEAS adopted this equation in preference to several other acceptable ones because it proved very accurate, and is completely in keeping with economic theory (specifically, the relationship between fleet size and Gross National Product is a common sense finding). It is a simple statistical equation, and all of the statistical tests normally applied to an analysis of this type yielded acceptable values. The standard error of the estimate of the coefficient is very low and the coefficient of correlation has the very high value of .996, indicating a high degree of explanation of the variation of the fleet population with GNP. The residuals (difference between the actual historical fleet size and the size as estimated by the equation) were very low, showing no apparent pattern to suggest other than a linear relationship.

Figure 5 demonstrates the closeness of the fit between the forecast model and the observed values.

The foregoing equation must be modified by the application of a 6.8 percent factor to account for the previously described adjustment of the 1967 total fleet population from the FAA eligible value to the active base of 122,200. This modification results in the final forecast equation:

$$Y = 1.068 (7.14 + .142X)$$

c) *Gross National Product*

Before a forecast of the fleet can be generated, it is necessary to obtain projections of the independent variable Gross National Product. The forecast of this value as used in the present study was obtained from the Economics Department of McGraw-Hill Publications. The GNP projections used can be found in their publication, "The American Economy — Prospects for Growth Through 1982".

Figure 5

COMPARISON OF ACTUAL AND COMPUTED
GENERAL AVIATION AIRCRAFT
1953-1967

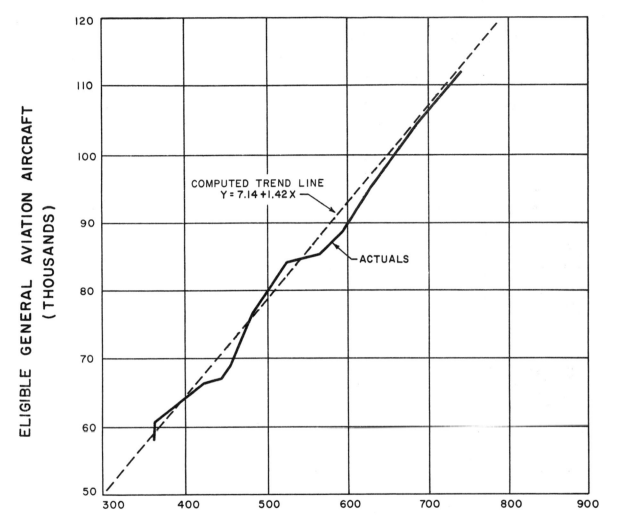

NOTE: TREND LINE IS BASED ON VALUES OF THE GNP FOR THE YEAR "X"
AND VALUES OF THE ACTIVE FLEET FOR YEAR "(X+I)".

SOURCE: SPEAS ANALYSIS USING FAA DATA

Figure 6

FORECAST OF U.S. GROSS NATIONAL PRODUCT

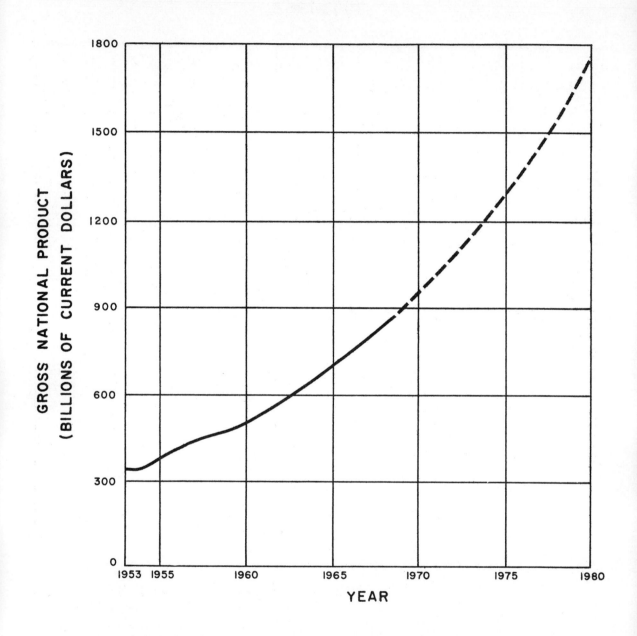

SOURCE: MC GRAW-HILL STUDY "THE AMERICAN ECONOMY PROSPECTS FOR
GROWTH THROUGH 1982" (CONSTANT DOLLAR FORECAST)

SPEAS ANALYSIS

The McGraw-Hill base forecast of GNP was in constant dollars, which had to be converted to current dollars for use in the fleet forecast equation. The inflation rate judged appropriate for this conversion was two percent per year, a figure which may prove conservative but which appears reasonable to SPEAS' economists and is supported by McGraw-Hill's views.

Figure 6 shows graphically the GNP forecast, including the two percent inflation in the general economy. This forecast is based upon what SPEAS considers to be reasonable assumptions by McGraw-Hill, as follows:

"First: Between now and 1972, the war in Vietnam will be settled."

Figure 7
GROSS NATIONAL PRODUCT AND GENERAL AVIATION FLEET POPULATION
— ACTUAL AND FORECAST —

Year	GNP Billions of Current Dollars	Population of the General Aviation Fleet	
		FAA Data[2] Eligible a.c.	SPEAS Estimate and Forecast[3] Active a.c.
Actual			
1953	365.4		
1954	363.1	61,290	
1955	398.0	58,790	
1956	419.2	62,886	
1957	442.8	66,520	
1958	447.3	67,839	
1959	482.1	68,727	
1960	503.8	76,550	
1961	520.1	80,632	
1962	560.3	84,121	
1963	590.5	85,088	
1964	631.7	88,742	
1965	681.2	95,442	
1966	739.6	104,706	
1967	793.5	114,186	122,200
1968	865.7	122,200	130,000
Forecast[1]			
1969	885.3		136,000
1970	939.7		143,000
1971	997.6		152,000
1972	1059.8		161,000
1973	1127.5		170,000
1974	1200.0		181,000
1975	1276.7		192,000
1976	1357.6		204,000
1977	1444.5		216,000
1978	1539.2		229,000
1979	1640.8		244,000
1980	1749.7		260,000

[1]GNP forecast includes 2% inflation in the general economy.
[2]FAA reported statistics.
[3]Based on SPEAS adjustment of base year data for 1967 and a one-year time lag correlation between GNP and the active fleet.
Source: FAA
       McGraw-Hill "The American Economy," June 1968.
       SPEAS Development and Analysis.
       Dept. of Commerce: "Survey of Current Business."

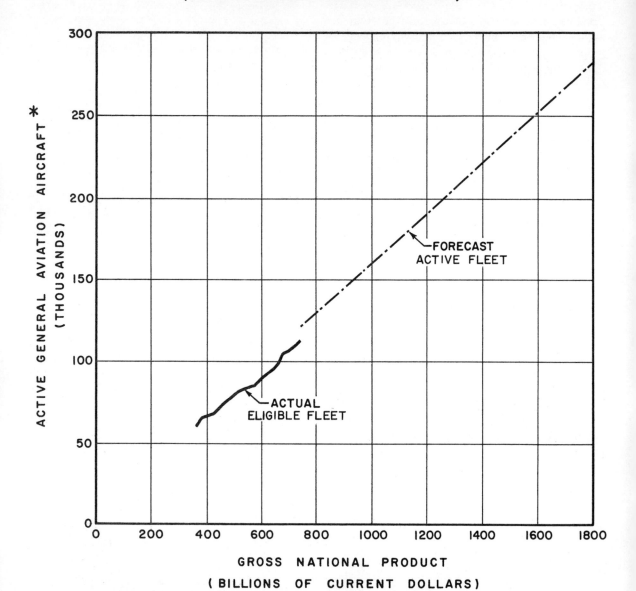

Figure 8

FORECAST OF GENERAL AVIATION AIRCRAFT
IN THE UNITED STATES
(GROSS NATIONAL PRODUCT PROJECTION)

NOTE: PROJECTION IS BASED ON VALUES OF THE GNP FOR THE YEAR "X"
AND VALUES OF THE ACTIVE FLEET FOR YEAR "(X+1)".

＊ SHOWING HISTORICAL FAA REPORTED DATA. FORECAST BASED ON
1967 ADJUSTED POPULATION OF 122,200 AIRCRAFT

SOURCE: SPEAS ANALYSIS

"Second: The settlement will result in a shifting of some expenditures going for defense to civilian projects, which will help wipe out the ghettos and improve the standard of living of low and no-income families."

"Third: Our balance of international payments problem will be eased through the introduction of new international credit arrangements."

"Fourth: Inflation will not get out of hand in the U.S. as it did in 1967 and in 1968."

"Fifth: Political intervention into our business system will continue but at about today's rate."

"Sixth: Critical shortages of basic materials will not occur during this period because of our rising volume of research and development work."

"Seventh: No member of the atom bomb club will blow up the world."

If these assumptions tend to produce a more optimistic view of the economy than may actually be realized, the conservative rate of inflation chosen will tend to be offsetting.

The GNP forecast and the corresponding forecast of the General Aviation fleet is shown in Figures 7 and 8. The GNP is expected to surpass the 1.0 trillion dollar mark by the end of 1972, and to reach a level of 1.7 trillion dollars by 1980. By this same year, the General Aviation fleet is calculated to double, reaching a level of 260,000 active aircraft.

d) *Confirmation of the Forecast Methodology*

The original methodology was elaborated before actual GNP data was available for 1967. Later revision and expansion of the original study showed that the actual figure for 1967 U.S. Gross National Product (in current dollars) was $793.5 billion, which when applied to the existing formula, produced a 1968 fleet size of 129,400. This figure compares favourably with the actual of 130,000, whereas the earlier study had predicted a fleet size of 128,000 on the basis of preliminary GNP data, indicating a figure of $785.1 million for 1967.

It would therefore appear that the model is slightly conservative and that the growth of the General Aviation fleet in 1968, compared with 1967, is slightly greater than had been forecast. Examination of the analyses set out in the initial study against data and results available one year later — including the example just stated — confirm the forecast equation.

Up to a point, the example cited above indicates that the formula adopted is sensitive to the rate of inflation. Tending to confirm this observation is the finding that current dollar G.N.P., and not constant dollar G.N.P., correlates most highly with the active fleet. During the period used as a base in establishing the correlation, the United States experienced an inflation rate over the long term of approximately 2 percent, and this rate is expected to continue as an average value during the forecast period.

In the 1969 report prepared for GAMA, SPEAS has re-evaluated the basic relationship used previously (and the forecast of GNP) from several other vantage points. The conclusion is that the original, long-term forecast of active registered aircraft is valid. Hence, the 1980 fleet projection remains at 260,000. Since these forecasts represent the long run trend versus the short run perturbations discussed above, the previous forecasts of the intervening years have also been retained and are considered reasonable.

It is important to note once again that these projections are based on the assumption that no new material constraints on the growth of General Aviation will develop. In fact, however, during 1969 several developments have tended to limit the demand for General Aviation services. An even greater number of limitations are expected before corrective action, when it is forthcoming, can be influential in reversing this trend at several of the major U.S. air transportation hubs.

Again, in this sense, the forecasts are a projection of potential demand, given the discretionary spending desires of individuals and the recognized utility of general aviation to U.S. businessmen.

4. *Forecast of Annual Sales of New General Aviation Aircraft*

Between the years 1957 through 1964, sales of new General Aviation aircraft in the United States remained relatively constant, averaging about 6,000 units annually. This lack of growth was abruptly ended in 1965 when domestic sales rose to more than 9,500 units and, in 1966, when a record 13,000 new airplanes were sold. This was more than twice the average number sold in the 1957-64 period. It is not surprising that this magnitude of growth in sales activity could not be maintained on more than a temporary basis. The manufacturers reporting to GAMA produced sales of only 10,451 airplanes for 1967,[8] well below 1966 but still ahead of the 1965 level. (See Figure 9).

During the same period, net additions to the total active fleet ranged between a low of 888 in 1959 to a high of 9,295 in 1966 (using FAA

[8]Total domestic sales, including non-GAMA members are estimated to have been 10,850 units.

published data). The erratic nature of the relationship between sales and net additions to the fleet, as expressed by the computed fleet retirements, merely cautions against placing too great emphasis on the significance of any single year's finding, especially in the earlier years shown.

Fleet retirements for 1965-67 averaged about 30 percent of sales and were even higher over the full 11 year history shown, as described earlier in this report. This ratio is expected to continue at approximately the 30-35 percent level through 1975 and decline to a lesser figure thereafter. In general, justification for this is based on the age composition of the present fleet and, specifically, upon the evolution of the all metal aircraft together with higher maintenance standards. The almost complete elimination of the large blocks of military surplus aircraft from the active fleet also has a bearing on this.

The implications of these factors will be offset by the growing affluence of the aircraft owners, which has in other industries (e.g., the

Figure 9

HISTORY AND PROJECTION OF DOMESTIC UNIT SALES OF GENERAL AVIATION AIRCRAFT — TOTAL FLEET

Fleet as of December 31

Year	FAA Data Eligible Aircraft	SPEAS Data Active Aircraft	Net Additions To The Fleet	Fleet Retirements	Domestic Unit Sales[1]
1957	66,520		3,634	1,597	5,231
1958	67,839		1,319	4,520	5,839
1959	68,727		888	6,134	7,022
1960	76,550		7,823	(1,158)	6,305
1961	80,632		4,082	1,115	5,197
1962	84,121		3,489	1,750	5,239
1963	85,088		967	5,023	5,990
1964	88,742		3,654	3,907	7,561
1965	95,442		6,700	2,826	9,526
1966	104,706		9,264	3,507	12,802
1967	114,186	122,200	9,480	1,190	10,850(E)
1975		192,000	11,000	7,260[2]	17,900
1980		260,000	15,000	7,250[2]	21,560

[1]Manufacturers reporting to the UAC through 1967; forecast for total industry.
[2]Based on individual aircraft retirement rates consistent with a past trend of approximately 30% for the total fleet and reflecting declining rates in the future.

Source: FAA Statistical Handbook of Aviation
        GAMA Production Records
        SPEAS Analysis

automobile industry), accelerated attrition, and the advancing technology in General Aviation aircraft, which has obsolesced much of the existing fleet in the past. The net result, however, is the prospect of a modest decline in the ratio of fleet retirements to domestic sales during the latter part of the forecast period.

This expectation is reflected in the forecast of sales of new aircraft. It is estimated that sales during the early part of the forecast period will remain relatively unchanged from the 1965-67 level so that by 1970 sales will approximate 12,730 units. The flatness of this near term projection reflects a period of adjustment and discounting of the unusually large influx of new aircraft into the active fleet since 1965. This sales volume is, nonetheless, almost double the 1957-64 average rate and about 5,000 units above the highest rate achieved during that period.

Even with a declining rate of retirements in the years after 1970, annual domestic sales will go up significantly during the decade 1971-1980. Based on the forecast of the total active fleet, which produces a projection of the net additions to the fleet, and the respective estimates of fleet retirements, domestic sales in 1975 will be 17,900 units and in 1980 will be 21,560. (See Figure 10). As can be seen, these forecasts maintain the growth rate in annual domestic sales generally established between 1957 and 1967. Sales doubled during the years 1957-67 and are expected to double again in the succeeding 12 year period.

It is important to note that this is a conservative estimate by comparison with the manufacturers' opinions and, were the forecast to be based on the same assumptions regarding the relative importance of each of the factors governing the retirement ratio as used by the manufacturers in their estimates, the 1980 domestic sales forecast would increase to over 23,000 units. This implies a rather radical change in customer buying power and habits as well as a revolutionary technological departure from the present level of General Aviation aircraft development. It is not foreseen that either of these will occur, but it is recognized that the impact of their doing so is possible and would result in a higher sales level than that forecast for the U.S.

Turning to exports of American built General Aviation aircraft, it is quite apparent that there is a fairly constant relationship between domestic sales and exports, although exports have grown to their present level at a more steady rate than domestic sales. (See Figure 11). In fact, exports as a percentage of domestic sales for the years 1960-67 show a relatively uniform ratio, varying between 20.3 percent and 30.4 percent — the average for the 8 years being 25 percent. The "B" extrapolation line on the following graph is based on 25 percent of the forecasted domestic sales and produces a 1980 forecast of exports of 5,390 aircraft. (See Figure 12).

Alternatively, it may be seen that the aberrations noted for domestic sales in the years 1965-1967 do not appear in the history of exports, which suggests that a more appropriate forecasting technique would be to extrapolate the past trend of the number of aircraft exported. It seems reasonable that exports would not vary with the domestic sales, except in some gross way, and that they would be a function of their own set of governing factors. This being accepted, the "A" extrapolation on the graph constitutes the forecast of the number of exports and produces a 1980 forecast of 5,500 units.

Figure 10
DOMESTIC UNIT SALES
OF
NEW GENERAL AVIATION AIRCRAFT

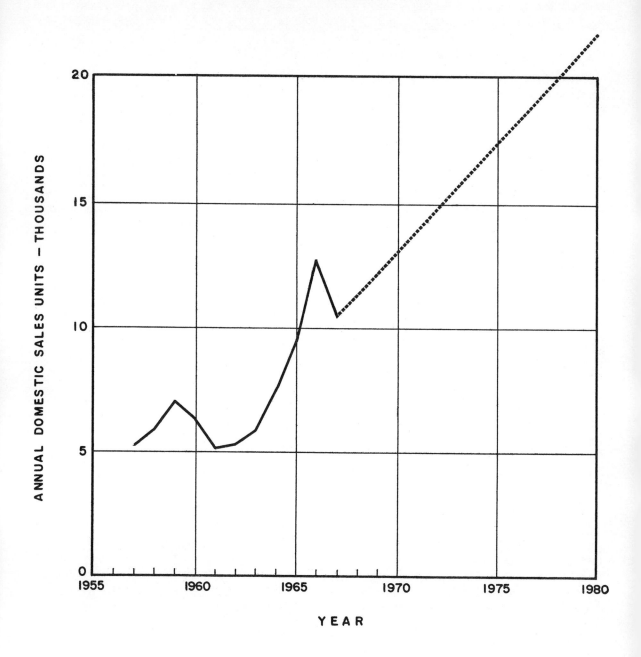

SOURCE: GAMA PRODUCTION RECORDS
SPEAS ANALYSIS

Figure 11

U.S. EXPORTS OF GENERAL AVIATION AIRCRAFT[1]

Year	Domestic Sales Units	Exports % of Domestic	Units	Total Sales by U.S. Manufacturers
1957	5,231	20.0%	887	6,118
1958	5,839	9.8	575	6,414
1959	7,022	9.5	667	7,689
1960	6,305	20.3	1,283	7,588
1961	5,197	30.4	1,581	6,778
1962	5,239	27.8	1,458	6,697
1963	5,990	26.4	1,579	7,569
1964	7,561	23.5	1,775	9,336
1965	9,526	24.4	2,326	11,852
1966	12,802	23.2	2,966	15,768
1967	10,451	29.7	3,036	13,487
1975	17,900	25.1	4,500[2]	22,400
1980	21,560	25.5	5,500[2]	27,060

[1]As reported by GAMA only
[2]Based on extrapolation of unit exports 1957-1967
Source: GAMA Records
          SPEAS Analysis

20

Figure 12
U.S. EXPORTS OF GENERAL AVIATION AIRCRAFT

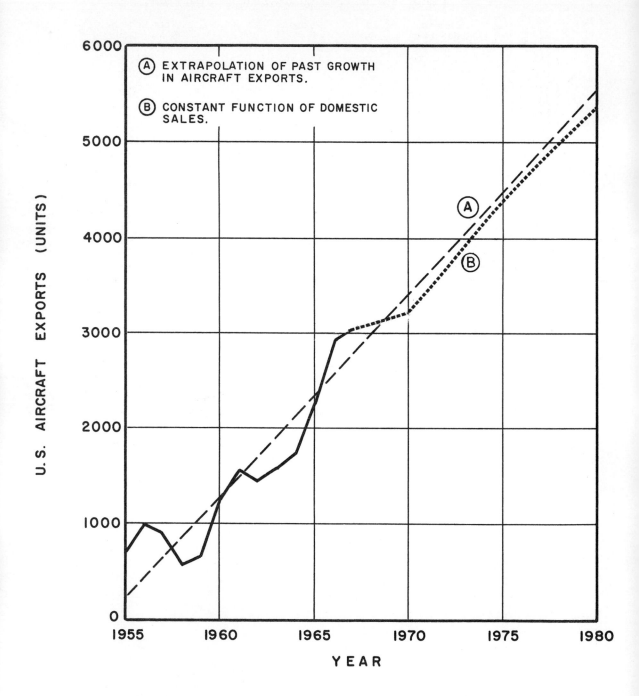

SOURCE: SPEAS ANALYSIS

CHAPTER TWO

GEOGRAPHICAL DISTRIBUTION OF
THE GENERAL AVIATION FLEET

The initial study undertaken by SPEAS in 1968 defined a methodology for ascertaining the potential distribution of the General Aviation fleet in 1975 and 1980. This showed the expected geographical distribution of the fleet among the top 75 Standard Metropolitan Statistical Areas (SMSAs) as ranked by population. The 1969 study refined the earlier work and provided what is perhaps the first in-depth analysis of forecasting the geographical distribution of the General Aviation fleet. In a sense, the 1969 revision reduces to an acceptable level the judgemental inputs required to produce a forecast.

For both the state and SMSA forecasts a mathematical approach was adopted. The final models used in the projections were the result of extensive experimentation in technique and in the selection of explanatory variables.

1. *Present Geographic Distribution*

The findings of an initial descriptive approach aimed at determining the factors which could help explain the geographic pattern of distribution, are shown in the accompanying maps which indicate the distribution by state and by SMSA.

The first map is purely descriptive and shows the distribution of the General Aviation fleet in the United States as of the year end 1967. The second map shows the ratio of active General Aviation aircraft per thousand households with incomes over $10,000 in each of the top 75 SMSAs.

The findings of this particular analysis indicate that there are five regions within the U.S. which appear to have approximately the same relationship between high income households and the number of registered aircraft. These

areas are shown graphically on Figure 14 with ratio values indicated for each city.

Northeast (Washington to Boston and west to the Appalachians). The range for the computed ratio (General Aviation aircraft per 1,000 households with income over $10,000) is from just below 2 to 3.5 for most cities. This area includes all those in the "megalopolitan" area from Boston to Washington, except Washington and Wilmington, which both have values over 6. Harrisburg and Allentown are also higher, having values of 7 and 5, respectively. There is a definite tendency for the small cities to have high rates in this Northeast region, and in most of the other regions, indicating that the convenience of small planes is to some extent negated in very large cities and that much of their use is to link smaller cities with the major national centers. It is easy to recognize Washington as an exceptional case, but it is less apparent as to why Harrisburg and Allentown show relatively high ratios.

Midwest (running west from the Appalachians to Minneapolis and St. Louis). Except for a few of the largest cities, the range in the ratio is from 3.7 to 8. Chicago, Cleveland, Detroit, and especially Buffalo fall below this. The western New York cities and Pittsburgh are grouped with the Midwest region, because they seem to bear a closer resemblance in rates than with the Northeast region.

Here, as in the Northeast, the smaller cities have the higher rates. Cities like Columbus, Indianapolis, and Grand Rapids show similar rates and have a common rank as medium-sized regional centers, from which rapid access to the major cities (Chicago, Cleveland, New York) represent a special demand. The ratio for Minneapolis seems low.

Figure 13

GEOGRAPHIC DISTRIBUTION OF ACTIVE
GENERAL AVIATION AIRCRAFT
12-31-67

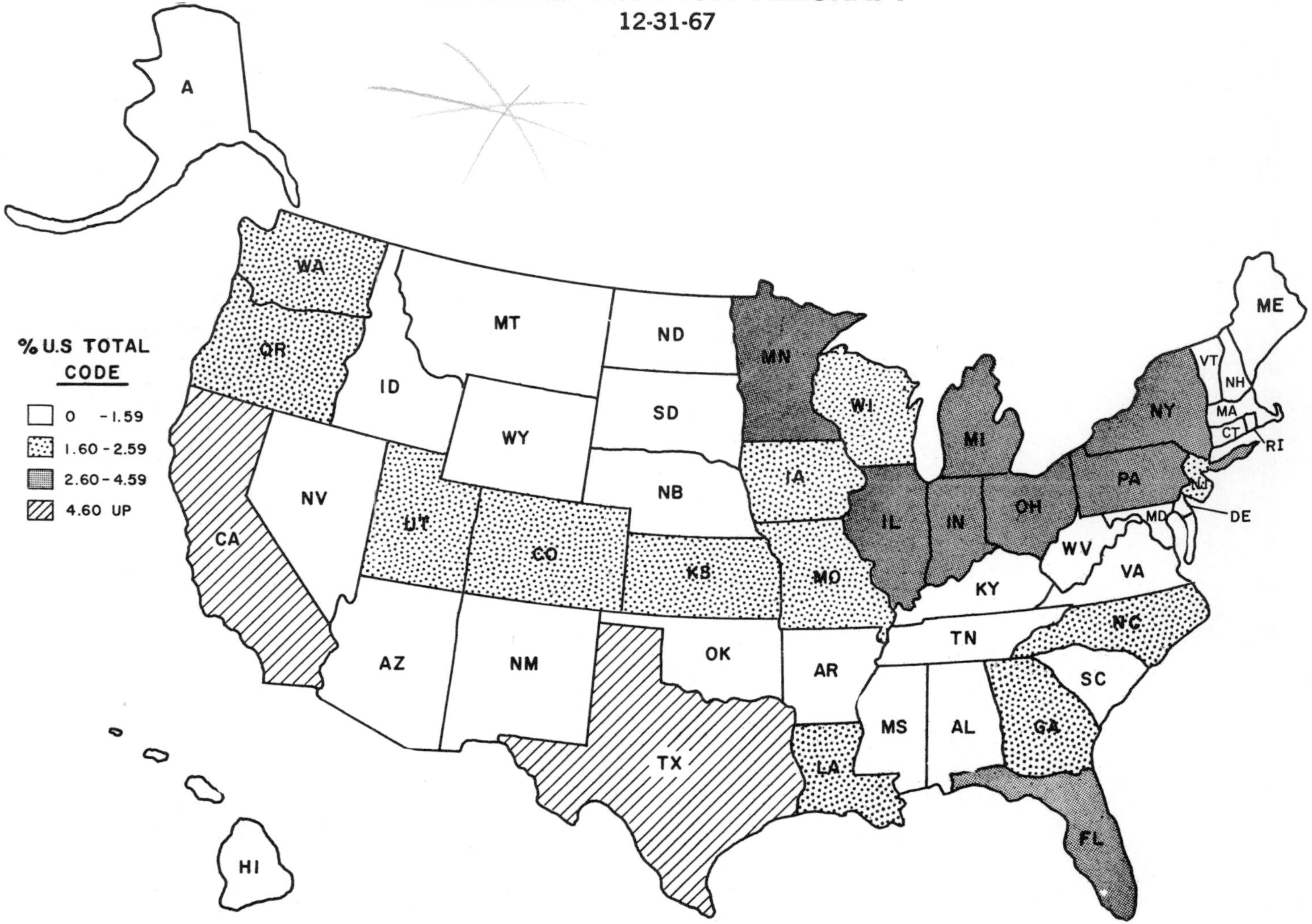

% U.S. TOTAL
CODE

☐	0 — 1.59
▦	1.60 — 2.59
▧	2.60 — 4.59
▨	4.60 UP

23

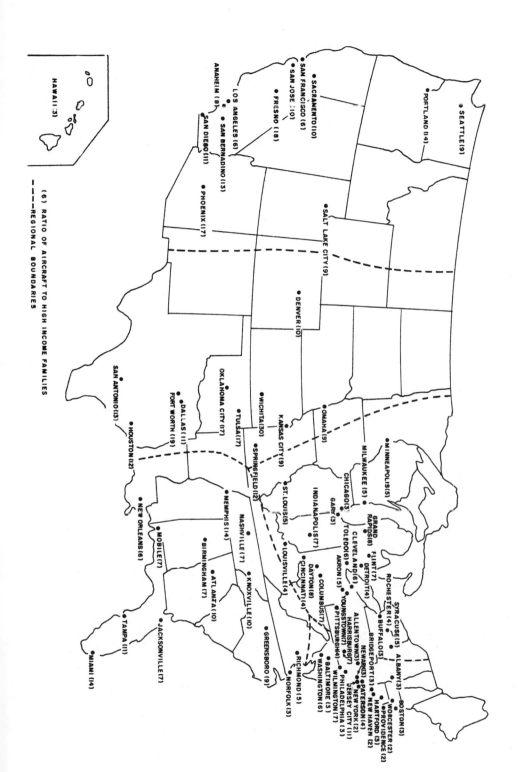

Figure 14

ACTIVE GENERAL AVIATION AIRCRAFT PER
1000 FAMILIES WITH INCOME OVER $10,000

(TOP 75 U.S. SMSAs RANKED BY POPULATION)

Great Plains (Omaha to Denver and south to Texas). Most cities in this region range from 9 to 13, with Oklahoma City and Tulsa both over 16, Fort Worth at 19, and Wichita at the rate of 30, (reflecting the location of General Aviation aircraft manufacturers). If Dallas and Fort Worth were combined, their rate would fall within the general range. In this region the large cities still rank a little lower than the smaller ones, but the differences tend to be less.

Southeast The ratio range is generally from 6 to 10, but there are a number of exceptions. Richmond and particularly Norfolk have lower rates, which match well with those of the Northeast (with which these cities are rarely associated, however). Norfolk tends to be an exception in other respects, due to the presence of important naval installations. Miami's high rate (14) is also an understandable exception. The Memphis rate matches well with that of the Texas cities. This is the only region in which the larger cities have rates as high as the smaller cities, although the "larger" cities are not truly large when compared with those of other regions.

West The large cities are in the 6 to 9 ratio range; the smaller ones spread from 10 to 18. Portland's ratio of 14 seems unusually high when compared with Seattle's 9. The very low figure for Honolulu (3) is easy to understand, but Salt Lake City (9) is perhaps lower than might be expected.

The foregoing findings indicate the existence of useful patterns and a quantitative measure of the relationship between high purchasing power and aircraft ownership which can be plotted on a demographic basis. The regional ratio ranges for the smaller cities scarcely overlap (except for the Southeast, which occupies a position between the Midwest and the two western areas).

2. *Methodology for Forecasting Fleet Distribution by State and by SMSA*

The models employed in forecasting the demand for General Aviation aircraft were of the cross-section, time-series variety. Such models depict relationships that hold over many individuals, in this case SMSAs and states, and over several periods of time. The objective was to estimate statistically a meaningful economic relationship representing the demand for General Aviation aircraft in many locations and over several years.

On the basis of such models a relationship was estimated for 65 of the 75 SMSAs studied; ten of the SMSAs would not conform to a generalized approach. After extensive experimentation the following independent variables were found to be significant:

- auto sales in millions of dollars. This variable reflects general economic conditions as well as tastes and other non-quantifiable factors.

- number of large cities, with a population greater than 100,000, within a radius of 200 miles of the SMSA center. This variable suggests the degree of urbanization around the SMSA and hence the distances involved in movement between urban centers in the area. The lesser the number of the cities, the greater the distances to be covered in connecting them and hence the greater the need for utility aircraft.

- a set of qualitative variables that represent the five regions suggested by Rand McNally in the demographic analysis of regions. The basic classification of the regions was undertaken according to the ratio:

No. of Aircraft ÷ No. of families with
income greater than
or equal to $10,000.

The equation and its statistical properties are given in Figure 15. The properties of the equation attest to its statistical soundness and its predictive capacity, given a continuation of the structural relationships observed in the past.

Figure 15

MULTIPLE REGRESSION EQUATION FOR THE SMSAs (65 Areas)

Variables:

$X_1 = $ Auto sales.

$X_2 = $ Number of large cities, population equal to or greater than 100,000, within a radius of 200 miles of the SMSA.

$X_3 - X_6 = $ Qualitative variables representing the Rand-McNally regions.

Equation:

$$Y = 525.8 + 1.2X_1 - 18.3X_2 - 264.0X_3 - 218.9X_4 - 356.5X_5 - 72.3X_6$$

Standard Deviations of Coefficients	T-Ratio	Beta Coefficients
.019	62.728	.88
2.466	−7.421	−.20
38.044	−6.940	−.20
28.524	−7.676	−.18
27.162	−13.128	−.23
27.855	−2.595	−.04

Standard error of estimate $= 161$

Coefficient of Multiple Correlation $= .957$

F level $= 810$

Degrees of Freedom $= (6,448)$

Durbin-Watson $= 1.644$

The next step in the methodology was to forecast the time-series independent variable — namely, auto sales. This was accomplished through the derivation of the least squares equation for the trend line (curve) of the time series of the independent variable per SMSA. By definition, the trend equation offers the *average* values of the independent variable at every point in time.

A more sophisticated approach to the forecasts of the independent variable is desirable but not critical. Projections of auto sales could not be obtained from outside sources and the scope of the present work limited investigation in this area. Auto sales are compatible in most cases with a time-series analysis at the SMSA level and such an approach was judged adequate.

The forecasted values of the independent variable, for each SMSA, were then substituted in the general equation to obtain forecasts of the demand for general aviation aircraft in 1975 and 1980. The forecasts were then corrected by an error factor which accorded heavier weights to recent years.

Ten SMSAs did not conform to any general pattern of behavior and were investigated separately through time-series trend equations and other methods. These SMSAs were: Buffalo, Honolulu, Louisville, Providence, Jersey City, Norfolk, Omaha, Jacksonville, Mobile and Salt Lake City. Again, in most cases, the forecast values for these SMSAs reflect only the average trend values.

A methodology essentially similar to that employed for the SMSAs was used in forecasting demand for aircraft by state. However, attempts to derive a single, general equation for all states failed. Consequently, the states were divided into eleven groups according to the general groupings employed in the U. S. Statistical Abstract and census data. An equation relevant to each group was then estimated. These equations and their statistical properties are given in the Appendix. The variables found to be generally significant were:

- number of families with income greater than $10,000
- number of households per state
- auto sales
- number of airports in the state
- number of large cities, population 100,000 or more, in the state
- special qualitative variables reflecting conditions particular to some states.

The methodology for forecasting the independent variables and deriving the aircraft mix are also similar to those employed in the SMSA study. Again a correction factor for predictive error of the equation, weighting the 1967 figures, was employed.

Findings

A history and the forecasts are presented in Figure 16 for the distribution by state and in Figure 17 by SMSA.

Apart from the individual projections, it is important to note that the top 75 SMSAs will collectively account for 50.6 percent of the U.S. total in 1980. This finding is down slightly from the previous research results of 51.7 percent. Most important, however, is the fact that both are considerably higher than the present level of 44 percent. The even greater concentration of general aviation aircraft in the metropolitan areas of the U. S. indicates where the primary focus and concentration of planning efforts must be placed.

As before, that area with the greatest concentration of general aviation aircraft is and will be Southern California, principally the Los Angeles metropolitan area. By 1980, it is projected that Los Angeles will have 9,000 registered aircraft. In 1968 it had 4,800. Anaheim will share in this growth, at an even higher rate of growth. Among the top 15, New York, Philadelphia, Detroit, Boston, San Francisco, St. Louis, Washington D.C. and Baltimore will more than double their fleets between 1968 and 1980.

Out of all 75 SMSAs, 12 will grow more than three times by 1980. A majority of these rapidly growing areas are to be found at the lower end of the list, as ranked by population. Although the greatest growth in terms of numbers of aircraft will occur in the largest metropolitan centers, the greatest growth in terms of percentage increase will occur in the smaller centers, at least between 1968 and 1980.

A similar pattern exists for the states. There was only one state in 1968 with more than 10,000 active aircraft registrations. California has about 17,400. By 1980, California will be joined by Texas, New York, Illinois and Florida. It is the smaller states, however, which will experience the higher growth rates.

Figure 16

ESTIMATED DISTRIBUTION OF THE GENERAL AVIATION FLEET IN THE UNITED STATES
— HISTORICAL AND POTENTIAL —

Region, State	Number of Eligible Registered Aircraft[1]							Number of Active Registered Aircraft			
	1960	1961	1962	1963	1964	1965	1966	1967[1]	1968[1]	1975	1980
New England											
Connecticut	556	589	602	629	659	692	861	1,055	1,120	1,600	2,100
Maine	391	381	409	402	392	438	486	530	575	800	1,000
Massachusetts	983	1,053	1,096	1,083	1,148	1,230	1,397	1,615	1,800	2,600	3,500
New Hampshire	199	218	218	224	211	263	288	355	375	600	800
Rhode Island	134	138	139	134	126	134	159	185	220	300	400
Vermont	99	127	124	126	145	172	206	260	280	400	500
Mid Atlantic											
New Jersey	1,465	1,558	1,660	1,685	1,796	2,053	2,317	2,650	2,810	5,200	7,600
New York	3,015	3,119	3,365	3,313	3,403	3,769	4,297	4,980	5,345	8,800	12,200
Pennsylvania	2,644	2,753	2,832	2,800	2,811	3,048	3,325	3,920	4,190	6,300	8,400
South Atlantic											
Delaware	254	262	271	279	306	314	401	490	555	800	1,100
District of Columbia	292	313	313	314	342	554	565	685	720	1,100	1,400
Florida	2,561	2,780	2,875	3,018	3,288	3,493	4,036	4,710	4,960	7,500	10,500
Georgia	1,089	1,181	1,218	1,300	1,361	1,554	1,826	2,350	2,615	4,300	6,400
Maryland	681	725	791	829	866	952	1,093	1,380	1,525	3,700	6,100
North Carolina	1,206	1,296	1,304	1,405	1,422	1,617	1,754	2,140	2,245	3,800	5,400
South Carolina	488	541	549	556	578	692	805	975	1,065	2,100	3,300
Virginia	897	944	966	971	1,102	1,243	1,347	1,545	1,710	2,600	3,800
West Virginia	396	467	474	458	464	447	486	500	580	800	1,100
East North Central											
Illinois	3,885	3,754	3,834	3,777	3,969	4,200	4,601	5,385	5,635	8,600	12,100
Indiana	2,130	2,353	2,455	2,422	2,472	2,535	2,757	3,205	3,330	5,000	6,900
Michigan	2,957	3,132	3,270	3,404	3,485	3,705	4,164	4,915	5,190	7,100	9,100
Ohio	3,412	3,543	3,654	3,710	3,807	4,147	4,528	5,290	5,560	7,600	9,500
Wisconsin	1,544	1,665	1,692	1,689	1,706	1,834	1,919	2,340	2,480	3,400	4,200
East South Central											
Alabama	770	883	929	927	1,072	1,201	1,324	1,600	1,670	2,300	3,000
Kentucky	633	659	678	672	697	703	760	885	985	1,300	1,800
Mississippi	870	924	975	980	988	1,111	1,213	1,400	1,460	2,100	2,800
Tennessee	891	977	1,019	1,096	1,143	1,237	1,360	1,690	1,750	2,400	3,300

(Continued on Next Page)

Figure 16

(Continued from Preceding Page)

Region, State	Number of Eligible Registered Aircraft[1]							Number of Active Registered Aircraft			
	1960	1961	1962	1963	1964	1965	1966	1967[1]	1968[1]	1975	1980
West North Central											
Iowa	1,698	1,784	1,758	1,744	1,809	1,911	2,150	2,455	2,540	3,100	4,600
Kansas	1,862	2,003	2,237	2,369	2,629	2,782	2,575	2,820	2,990	4,200	5,500
Minnesota	2,127	2,236	2,277	2,259	2,386	2,435	2,680	3,215	3,410	4,800	6,300
Missouri	1,738	1,834	1,897	1,910	2,050	1,111	1,213	3,020	3,240	4,800	6,500
Nebraska	1,291	1,373	1,381	1,384	1,289	1,362	1,438	1,685	1,775	2,600	3,500
North Dakota	677	701	694	695	740	764	819	1,005	1,035	1,700	2,400
South Dakota	834	873	810	791	729	775	809	935	885	1,700	2,300
West South Central											
Arkansas	992	1,015	1,081	1,161	1,290	1,397	1,740	1,635	1,740	2,900	4,000
Louisiana	1,267	1,315	1,382	1,386	1,441	1,530	1,747	2,010	2,145	3,400	4,800
Oklahoma	1,693	1,796	1,938	1,905	2,012	2,129	2,377	2,520	2,885	4,000	5,100
Texas	6,719	6,905	7,110	7,072	7,240	7,819	8,346	9,505	9,945	14,400	19,200
Mountain											
Arizona	1,228	1,332	1,448	1,450	1,493	1,461	1,576	1,900	2,060	2,700	3,100
Colorado	1,034	1,166	1,233	1,276	1,251	1,411	1,659	2,020	2,180	3,100	3,900
Idaho	748	750	821	888	892	929	980	1,100	1,140	1,700	2,200
Montana	1,052	1,051	1,132	1,146	1,200	1,197	1,286	1,475	1,510	2,200	2,900
Nevada	433	472	520	595	615	707	838	940	985	1,500	2,000
New Mexico	909	1,013	1,040	1,032	1,002	1,089	1,136	1,230	1,290	1,900	2,400
Utah	515	546	613	615	597	582	685	735	770	1,500	2,200
Wyoming	451	509	557	531	544	534	567	620	620	800	1,000
Pacific											
California	9,884	10,412	10,982	11,226	12,140	12,936	14,043	16,490	17,405	24,900	33,800
Oregon	1,533	1,597	1,690	1,718	1,802	1,924	2,228	2,620	2,680	3,700	4,800
Washington	1,820	1,913	1,973	1,919	1,970	2,177	2,354	2,840	3,230	3,900	4,900
Alaska	1,391	1,449	1,525	1,488	1,476	1,600	1,717	1,815	2,100	2,400	2,800
Hawaii	77	88	107	112	136	146	145	175	190	300	600
Total United States	76,415	80,468	83,918	84,875	88,492	95,176	104,378	121,800	129,500	191,300	259,100
Other (Outside U.S.)	113	134	164	213	250	266	328	400	500	700	900
Total Fleet Registrations	76,528	80,602	84,082	85,088	88,742	95,442	104,706	122,200	130,000	192,000	260,000

Notes: The forecasts assume no new material constraints on the growth of general aviation. As such, they are projections of potential demand.

Totals may not add due to rounding.
[1]Adjusted to reflect active aircraft. 1960-1966 data cover eligible aircraft only.

Source: FAA, Census of Aircraft, Years Shown 1960-1966.
FAA, Master Aircraft Register 31 March 1968 and 31 March 1969.
SPEAS Analysis.

Figure 17

ESTIMATED DISTRIBUTION OF THE GENERAL AVIATION FLEET
IN THE TOP 75 STANDARD METROPOLITAN STATISTICAL AREAS (SMSA)
— HISTORICAL AND POTENTIAL —

SMSA Area	Number of Eligible Registered Aircraft								Number of Active Registered Aircraft			
	1960	1961	1962	1963	1964	1965	1966	1967[1]	1968[1]	1975	1980
New York	1,335	1,386	1,489	1,454	1,504	1,605	1,898	2,196	2,415	3,700	4,800
Chicago	1,987	1,894	1,831	1,865	2,014	2,177	2,390	2,883	2,909	4,200	5,500
Los Angeles	2,909	3,026	3,148	3,216	3,548	3,769	4,014	4,596	4,813	6,900	9,000
Philadelphia	893	920	952	970	924	1,074	1,145	1,348	1,487	2,400	3,500
Detroit	1,070	1,120	1,205	1,185	1,229	1,298	1,509	1,746	1,821	3,100	4,100
Boston	501	571	580	579	615	660	771	865	958	1,400	1,900
San Francisco	1,140	1,113	1,221	1,216	1,279	1,443	1,656	2,037	2,085	3,500	5,100
Pittsburgh	482	514	533	545	484	513	551	719	816	1,200	1,500
St. Louis	670	683	715	721	724	804	949	1,067	1,077	1,900	2,700
District of Columbia	626	706	740	764	889	1,173	1,303	1,507	1,738	3,100	5,100
Cleveland	532	545	551	554	521	626	684	792	849	1,300	1,700
Baltimore	368	364	392	399	404	420	461	598	598	1,600	2,700
Newark	346	356	358	358	405	434	504	606	630	1,000	1,300
Minneapolis	882	957	952	926	1,021	1,024	1,176	1,439	1,510	2,600	3,600
Houston	879	895	908	898	1,076	1,194	1,383	1,501	1,455	2,400	3,200
Buffalo	230	233	251	241	226	253	251	294	329	500	600
Milwaukee	434	459	471	475	473	516	553	655	709	1,200	1,700
Cincinnati	334	354	376	360	363	381	428	426	440	700	800
Paterson	333	338	345	343	371	448	494	541	591	1,200	2,100
Dallas	886	926	892	896	904	1,021	1,095	1,390	1,486	2,200	3,300
Seattle	655	712	722	728	821	801	851	1,122	1,325	1,800	2,500
Kansas City	630	626	641	685	729	814	898	1,088	1,196	1,800	2,700
San Diego	575	578	585	611	659	708	741	982	1,061	1,500	2,200
Atlanta	475	469	478	522	576	673	818	1,087	1,151	2,000	3,400
Indianapolis	441	466	511	550	620	545	689	804	804	1,400	1,900
Miami	643	630	643	607	670	747	889	1,009	1,039	1,800	2,700
Denver	449	539	556	589	592	679	845	1,023	1,102	1,500	1,800
New Orleans	238	216	253	234	256	268	313	403	410	500	800
Portland	596	610	649	693	755	806	988	1,136	1,141	1,800	2,700
San Bernadino	531	566	532	646	676	818	947	1,029	1,071	1,500	2,000

(Continued on Next Page)

Figure 17

(Continued from Preceding Page)

SMSA Area	Number of Eligible Registered Aircraft								Number of Active Registered Aircraft		
	1960	1961	1962	1963	1964	1965	1966	1967'	1968'	1975	1980
Tampa	237	277	287	301	332	317	366	451	452	800	1,300
Columbus	301	339	325	336	394	413	477	527	559	1,100	1,700
Rochester	205	222	338	231	257	278	297	344	364	700	1,100
Dayton	366	374	379	383	417	429	468	477	580	900	1,300
Louisville	206	210	186	188	179	194	218	252	264	400	600
Birmingham	171	191	184	181	187	209	233	267	251	500	700
Providence	115	107	110	103	93	100	124	128	151	200	200
San Antonio	354	400	389	358	362	390	401	473	458	700	800
Anaheim	430	482	534	572	646	686	765	985	1,140	2,200	3,500
Hartford	159	167	177	186	165	209	253	287	298	500	800
Memphis	282	302	305	330	373	410	462	576	574	1,000	1,600
Phoenix	637	695	759	757	781	760	848	1,010	1,142	1,600	2,000
New Haven	115	117	114	108	126	120	148	161	182	300	400
Albany	144	160	151	147	152	183	202	232	266	500	800
Bridgeport	139	149	152	158	178	178	232	274	335	500	600
San Jose	378	443	524	591	694	797	930	1,076	1,121	2,100	3,300
Toledo	182	204	218	220	227	233	248	345	350	500	700
Sacramento	495	545	580	585	612	596	662	735	786	1,500	2,400
Jersey City	31	35	42	36	38	38	42	46	44	100	100
Akron	188	186	206	218	210	245	277	314	352	500	700
Worcester	121	128	140	128	136	143	187	211	234	300	400
Norfolk	98	91	100	94	94	95	105	105	113	200	200
Gary	187	289	283	253	181	185	175	195	256	400	600
Fort Worth	443	447	447	485	529	577	630	774	896	1,200	1,500
Syracuse	189	189	199	187	178	199	243	284	291	500	600
Springfield	126	119	119	132	132	171	141	177	203	400	500
Greensboro	263	296	270	277	300	321	334	404	426	800	1,400
Oklahoma City	399	410	491	522	566	563	600	673	732	1,000	1,400
Youngstown	198	193	199	198	200	210	222	240	243	400	500
Honolulu	63	72	83	95	111	111	112	149	160	200	300
Allentown	144	139	141	137	124	119	149	163	193	300	500
Nashville	150	140	154	161	165	176	182	237	224	400	600
Grand Rapids	191	217	211	227	268	259	284	349	345	600	800
Omaha	296	314	331	315	303	309	348	406	462	600	800
Jacksonville	134	151	159	130	145	151	180	200	208	300	400

(Continued on Next Page)

Figure 17

(Continued from Preceding Page)

SMSA Area	Number of Eligible Registered Aircraft							Number of Active Registered Aircraft			
	1960	1961	1962	1963	1964	1965	1966	1967[1]	1968[1]	1975	1980
Salt Lake City	234	248	238	276	273	264	296	348	348	600	800
Richmond	135	146	143	154	161	159	165	190	172	400	600
Tulsa	526	447	548	494	489	515	583	553	605	800	1,000
Flint	157	164	180	183	183	266	252	335	343	500	700
Wilmington	200	193	199	207	206	231	299	366	418	900	1,600
Wichita	578	576	660	847	1,064	1,157	867	868	901	1,500	1,800
Harrisburg	153	143	124	114	140	135	151	194	197	500	1,000
Knoxville	96	96	100	99	104	107	144	215	191	200	300
Fresno	343	356	348	333	378	382	416	478	501	700	800
Mobile	65	72	72	68	87	99	112	148	162	300	500
SMSA Total	32,676	34,013	35,539	35,935	38,268	41,341	45,934	54,111	57,509	92,300	131,200
Other Areas	43,739	46,455	48,379	48,940	50,224	53,835	58,444	67,689	71,991	99,000	127,900
Total 50 States	76,415	80,468	83,918	84,875	88,492	95,176	104,378	121,800	129,500	191,300	259,100
Total U.S. Fleet								122,200	130,000	192,000	260,000
Top 75 SMSA Percent of 50 States	42.8%	42.3%	42.3%	42.3%	43.2%	43.4%	44.0%	44.4%	44.4%	48.2%	50.6%

Notes: The forecasts assume no new material constraints on the growth of general aviation. As such, they are projections of potential demand.
Totals may not add due to rounding.

[1]Adjusted to reflect active aircraft. 1960-1966 data cover eligible aircraft only.

Source: SPEAS Analysis.

CHAPTER THREE

FLEET COMPOSITION BY AIRCRAFT TYPE

In a preceding chapter, the size of the total General Aviation fleet was forecast through to 1975 and 1980 using a macroanalysis approach.

An analysis and evaluation was also undertaken to determine the approximate size of the following groups of aircraft types or categories which comprise the total fleet:

Reciprocating Engine

(1) Single Engine, 1-3 Place
(2) Single Engine, 4+ Place
(3) Multi-Engine, to 12,500 lbs., to 600 HP
(4) Multi-Engine, to 12,500 lbs., over 600 HP
(5) Multi-Engine, over 12,500 lbs.

Turbine Engine

(6) Turboprop Single and Multi-Engine, to 12,500 lbs.
(7) Turboprop Single and Multi-Engine, over 12,500 lbs.
(8) Turbo-Jet
(9) *Rotorcraft*
(10) *Unspecified or Other*

The purpose of this determination — as in the case of the total fleet — was to forecast the population values primarily for the 1975 and 1980 time points, following the establishment of the 1967/68 adjusted fleet sizes. A micro-analysis of the 1969/70 time period was not considered relevant to the general objective of the study which was to measure the longer range size and impact of General Aviation.

In order to develop a forecast of the population of the individual categories of aircraft in the total active fleet, it was necessary to develop and use the following principal aids and determinants:

(1) The total fleet population boundaries as described earlier; that is,

1967 = 122,200
1968 = 130,000
1975 = 192,000
1980 = 260,000

(2) The 1955-1967 historical trends and the 1967 basic population value of the individual categories of aircraft as shown in the following Figures. (Note that these Figures also contain the projections to 1980 as they are developed in subsequent paragraphs).

(3) The 1955-1967 historical trends of important derived indices, including:

- Percentage growth rates by years for each available aircraft category, also as shown in subsequent Figures.
- Composition of the fleet mix, expressed as percentages of the total General Aviation fleet for each available aircraft category, as shown in later Figures.

(4) General transportation data available from the industry (General Aviation, Air Carrier, and U. S. business sources).

(5) Contractor background experience and in-house information.

Using these inputs, together with derived evaluations and judgments, estimates were prepared of the future fleet populations for each of the aircraft categories under consideration.

1. *Distribution of Active Fleet by Category*

a) *Reciprocating Single Engine 1-3 Place Aircraft*

During the period 1955-1967, this category of aircraft displayed the following population characteristics as indicated in the figures in this section:

	1955	1967*
Population Count	35,740	39,010
% Growth (12 years)		9.1
Annual % Growth (Compound)		0.7
% Share of Total G. A. Fleet	60.8	34.1

*SPEAS estimate of 1967 "eligible" fleet, unadjusted for "active" fleet determination, as shown in 1968 report.

These data indicate the relatively stable fleet size over the past thirteen years and its drop in terms of share of the total General Aviation fleet — reflecting the effect of high attrition rates and the trend towards the purchase of larger and more expensive aircraft. The single engine 1-3 place fleet is forecast to grow slightly and uniformly at an annual compound rate of 2.7 percent between 1967 and 1980. The following Figures 18-19 graphically portray this growth, indicating light consumer interest in small aircraft in an increasingly affluent society. Following is a summary of the forecast trend:

	1967*	1975	1980
Population Count	41,760	55,400	58,700
% Growth (13 years)			40.6
Annual % Growth (Compound)			2.7
% Share of Total G. A. Fleet	34.2	28.9	22.6

*Values adjusted for "Active Fleet" determination.

b) *Reciprocating Single Engine 4+ Place Aircraft*

Principal historical data references for the 1955-1967 time period indicate the following:

	1955	1967*
Population Count	19,240	57,887
% Growth (13 years)		200.9
Annual % Growth (Compound)		9.6
% Share of Total G. A. Fleet	32.7	50.6

*SPEAS estimate of 1967 "eligible" fleet, unadjusted for "active" fleet determination, as shown in 1968 report.

The "four and over" place single engine aircraft family has shown a fairly uniform growth rate during the past twelve years, as reflected by the straight line on the log scale graph in Figure 18. This steady increase is attributable to increased affluence in the U. S. and the pronounced preference for larger, more powerful and more versatile aircraft. There appears to be, however, some indication of a decreased rate of growth in terms of percentage of the total General Aviation fleet. Also, during the last six years (1962-1968) the approximate yearly growth rate has decreased, compared with the prior six years (1956-1962) from 12 percent to 7 percent.

It is forecast that the population of the 4+ place family of aircraft will continue to grow at just below its recent rate to a total of approximately 143,900 by 1980. Higher personal income, more leisure time, and broader acceptance of personal flying by families are factors which will contribute to the growth in fleet size. Also, it is visualized that 4 place aircraft will be used in increasing volume for training and instructional purposes. Following is a summary of the forecast trend:

	1967*	1975	1980
Population Count	61,319	98,200	143,900
% Growth (13 years)			134.7
Annual % Growth (Compound)			6.8
% Share of Total G. A. Fleet	50.2	51.1	55.3

*Values adjusted for "Active Fleet" determination.

c) *Reciprocating Multi-Engine Under 12,500 lbs., Under 600 HP*

This particular category is part of the total multi-engine family which also consists of aircraft "over 600 HP" and aircraft "over 12,500 lbs.". Consideration of the relationship between these three categories is relevant to forecasting the population of any of them. Precise historical reference data is not available for the two 600 HP categories under consideration, since FAA data is all on an 800 HP basis.

Historically, the "under 12,500 lb." aircraft category (based on FAA data for aircraft under and over 800 HP) has shown a compound annual growth rate of over 12% for the time period prior to 1965. However, the growth rate for all reciprocating multi-engine aircraft during the 1962-1967 time period was approximately 9 percent; this lower value is attributable to the absence of growth in the "over 12,500 lbs." category of aircraft.

It is forecast that there will be a continued substantial growth rate for the two "under 12,500 lbs." categories of aircraft. This growth will arise from the increasing interest in larger twin engine equipment, improved engines, and the ability of private owners to pay higher prices. On a "share-of-the-market" basis, however, it is not anticipated that these two aircraft categories will witness much change.

The population value for 1967, as derived from special programming of the FAA computer tapes for 1967 (and as adjusted by the

Figure 18
GENERAL AVIATION
ACTIVE FLEET POPULATION
(SINGLE-ENGINE, RECIPROCATING)

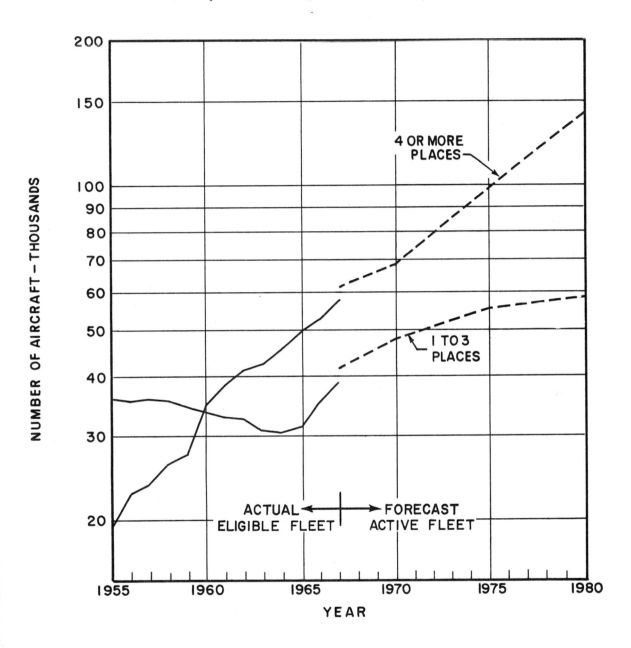

SOURCE: SPEAS ANALYSIS

Figure 19

ANNUAL PERCENTAGE GROWTH RATE OF ACTIVE FLEET
BY TYPE OF AIRCRAFT
SINGLE-ENGINE, RECIPROCATING

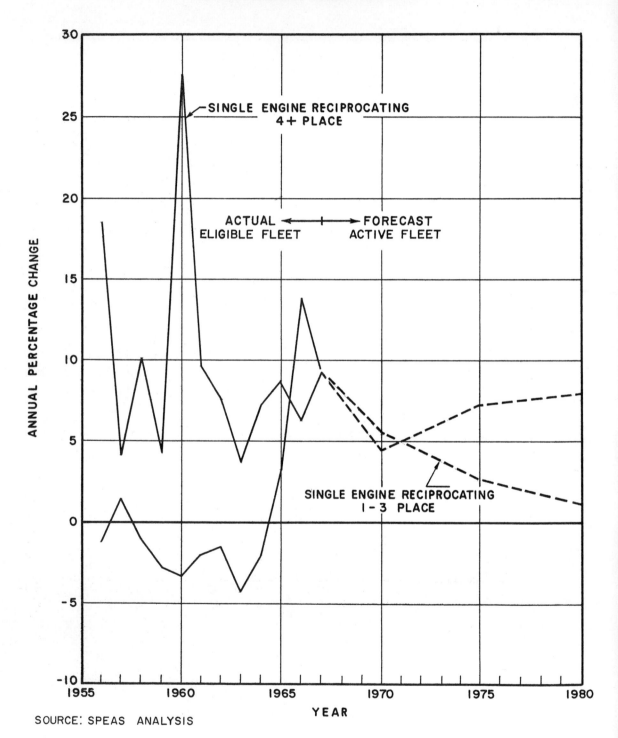

SOURCE: SPEAS ANALYSIS

full "active fleet" evaluation) is 10,423, as shown in an earlier Figure.

Application of the evaluation logic previously described results in projected values for the "under 600 HP" category as follows:

	1967*	1975	1980
Population Count	10,423	19,500	26,000
% Growth (13 years)			149.4
Annual % Growth (Compound)			7.3
% Share of Total G. A. Fleet	8.5	10.2	10.0

*Values adjusted for "Active Fleet" determination.

d) *Reciprocating Multi-Engine Under 12,500 lbs. Over 600 HP*

The 1967 value for active aircraft, as developed from the special programming process using FAA source tapes, is 2,864. The growth rates, market share, and population projection for the 1967-1980 time period is summarized as follows:

	1967*	1975	1980
Population Count	2,864	6,200	8,700
% Growth (13 years)			203.8
Annual % Growth (Compound)			8.9
% Share of Total G. A. Fleet	2.4	3.2	3.3

*Values adjusted for "Active Fleet" determination.

e) *Reciprocating Multi-Engine Over 12,500 lbs.*

The population of large (over 12,500 lbs. and over 800 HP) piston engine aircraft ceased to increase in 1961 and since that time has shown a decline. This fact is attributable to the widescale introduction of turbine engine equipment in the larger aircraft field. Prospective buyers of large size General Aviation aircraft are companies or individuals who have the financial means to select high performance equipment.

New large piston engine aircraft are not being manufactured. As a result, the size of the fleet is diminishing, and it is expected that the rate of decrease will become more rapid after 1968. It is forecast that this fleet category will decrease as indicated by the following indices:

	1967*	1975	1980
Population Count	1,222	800	500
% Decrease (13 years)			(59.1)
Annual % Decrease (Compound)			(6.8)
% Share of Total G. A. Fleet	1.0	0.4	0.2

*Values adjusted for "Active Fleet" determination.

f) *Reciprocating Multi-Engine*

The performance of the whole fleet of reciprocating multi-engine aircraft is the sum result of the three prior sub-categories just discussed.

Historically, the characteristics of the total population have been as follows:

	1955	1967*
Population Count	3,342	13,842
% Growth (12 years)		314.2
Annual % Growth (Compound)		12.6
% Share of Total G. A. Fleet	5.7	11.3

*SPEAS estimate of 1967 "eligible" fleet, unadjusted for "active" fleet determination, as shown in 1968 report.

As noted earlier the 1962-1967 growth rate has decreased to approximately 9 percent from the much higher 1955-1961 rate.

The 1967-1980 total fleet characteristic is as follows:

	1967*	1975	1980
Population Count	14,509	26,500	35,200
% Growth (13 years)			142.6
Annual Growth (Compound)			7.1
% Share of Total G. A. Fleet	11.9	13.8	13.5

*Values adjusted for "Active Fleet" determination.

(Figures 20 and 21 follow)

Figure 20

GENERAL AVIATION
ACTIVE FLEET POPULATION
(MULTI-ENGINE, RECIPROCATING)

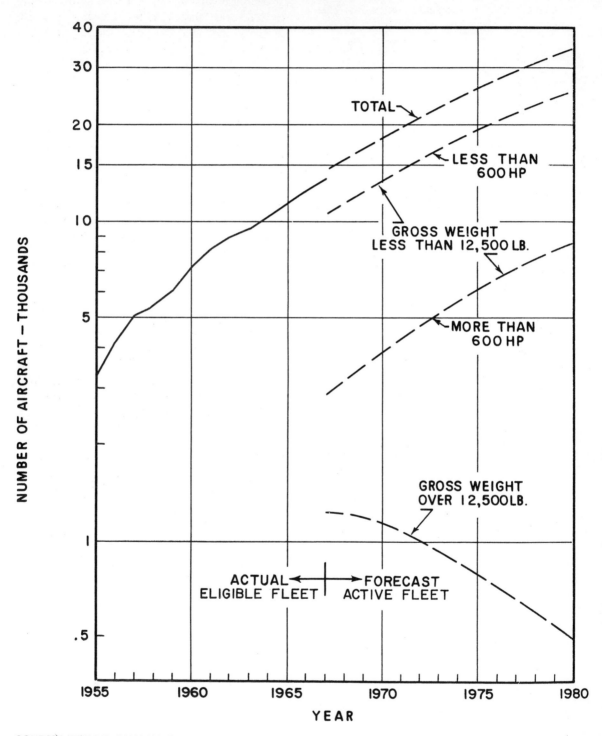

SOURCE: SPEAS ANALYSIS

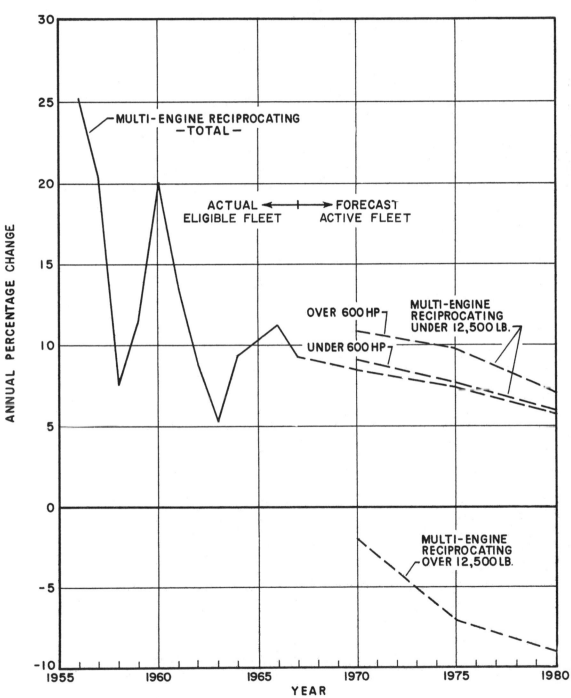

Figure 21   39

ANNUAL PERCENTAGE GROWTH RATE OF ACTIVE FLEET
BY TYPE OF AIRCRAFT
MULTI-ENGINE, RECIPROCATING

SOURCE: SPEAS ANALYSIS

g) *Turboprop Under 12,500 lbs.*

During the last few years, small turboprop aircraft have been introduced with great success. Air taxi operators, as well as corporations and private individuals, are finding that this category of aircraft meets the increasing desire of an affluent society for more comfortable and advanced technology transportation.

Buyers who previously would have purchased piston engine equipment will be acquiring "small" turboprops. It is anticipated that a 1967-1980 compound growth rate of approximately 20 percent will be achieved. Growth during this period is expected to be as follows, starting with a 1967 population of 475 aircraft developed from computer analyses of FAA data:

	1967*	1975	1980
Population Count	475	2,400	4,800
% Growth (13 years)			910.5
Annual Growth (Compound)			19.5
% Share of Total G. A. Fleet	0.4	1.2	1.9

*Values adjusted for "Active Fleet" determination.

h) *Turboprop Over 12,500 lbs.*

Turboprop aircraft in the "over 12,500 lb." category were introduced into General Aviation operations prior to the "under 12,500 lb." class. These included the Gulfstream I and the F-27. The 1967 computer derived active fleet value is 323 (versus 475 for the smaller turboprop category). There is far less relative interest in the larger turboprop class of aircraft today because suitably sized (albeit somewhat smaller) pure jet aircraft can offer more performance and comfort for modest differences in price.

The lower historical growth of this class, as compared with the "under 12,500 lb." category, is expected to continue. It is projected that the following values will describe the 1967-1980 period for these aircraft:

	1967*	1975	1980
Population Count	323	1,000	1,900
% Growth (13 years)			488.2
Annual % Growth (Compound)			14.6
% Share of Total G. A. Fleet	.3	.5	.7

*Values adjusted for "Active Fleet" determination.

i) *Turbo-Jet*

Pure jet type aircraft have shown a rapid growth rate. It is calculated that the December 31, 1967, adjusted population was 787 aircraft, or about equal to the total of all turboprop aircraft at that time.

It is expected that the rate of growth will continue to be high because of the demonstrated appeal of this equipment and the growth in corporate affluence, and in that of both commercial operators and individuals. Following are the projected characteristics of this market:

	1967*	1975	1980
Population Count	787	2,600	4,900
% Growth (13 years)			522.6
Annual % Growth (Compound)			15.1
% Share of Total G. A. Fleet	0.6	1.4	1.9

*Values adjusted for "Active Fleet" determination.

j) *Total Turbine Aircraft Fleet*

The total fleet characteristics of turboprop and pure jet aircraft are the result of the foregoing sub-categories. The FAA historical data is as follows:

	1961	1967*
Population Count	160	1,030
% Growth (16 years)		543.8
Annual % Growth (Compound)		36.0
% Share of Total G. A. Fleet	0.2	0.9

*SPEAS estimate of 1967 "eligible" fleet, unadjusted for "active" fleet determination, as shown in 1968 report.

Following are the projected values:

	1967*	1975	1980
Population Count	1,585	6,000	11,600
% Growth (13 years)			631.9
Annual % Growth (Compound)			16.6
% Share of Total G. A. Fleet	1.3	3.1	4.5

*Values adjusted for "Active Fleet" determination.

(Figures 22 and 23 follow)

Figure 22
GENERAL AVIATION
ACTIVE FLEET POPULATION
(TURBINE POWERED AIRCRAFT)

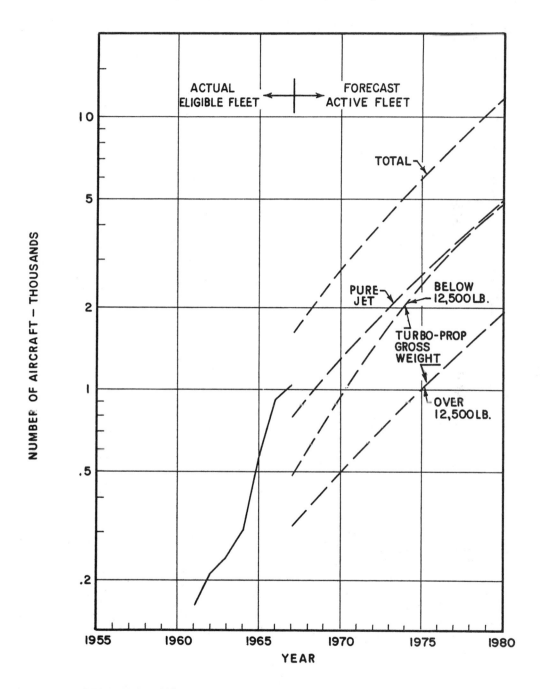

SOURCE: SPEAS ANALYSIS

Figure 23
ANNUAL PERCENTAGE GROWTH RATE OF ACTIVE FLEET
BY TYPE OF AIRCRAFT
TURBINE POWERED

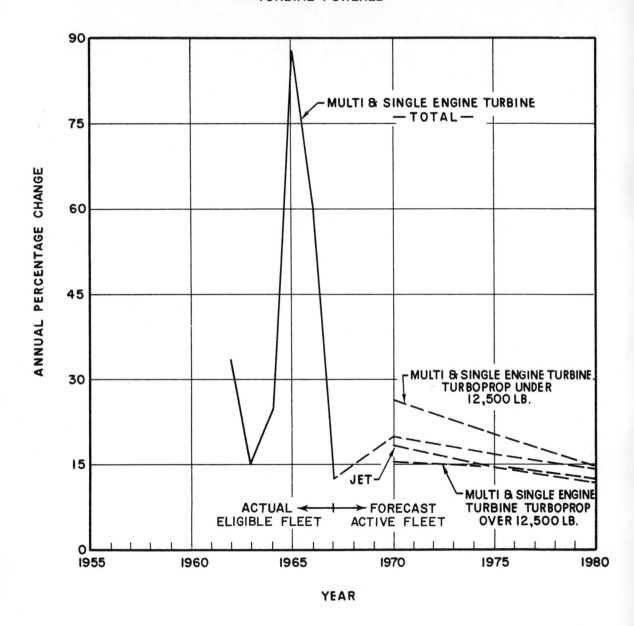

SOURCE: SPEAS ANALYSIS

k) *Rotor Aircraft*

Rotor Aircraft displayed a very constant and consistent yearly growth rate in excess of 20 percent from 1955 through 1963. Since 1963 the rate has fallen appreciably, primarily because Vietnam war requirements have absorbed most available production. This history can be summarized as follows:

	1955	1963
Population Count	237	1,171
% Growth (8 years)		394.1
Annual % Growth (Compound)		22.0
% Share of Total G. A. Fleet	0.4	1.4

It is projected that the backlog demand for helicopters (deferred because of Vietnam), plus the very major technological design advances made during recent years, the great recognition provided by wartime publicity, national affluence factors, as well as future technological and economic improvements will result in an increasing growth rate to 1980.

The forecasted population characteristics are as follows:

	1967*	1975	1980
Population Count	1,875	4,200	8,700
% Growth (13 years)			241.3
Annual % Growth (Compound)			12.5
% Share of Total G. A. Fleet	1.3	3.1	4.5

*Values adjusted for "Active Fleet" determination.

l) *"Other" Aircraft*

This classification includes primarily glider aircraft. The history of this equipment is as follows:

	1955	1967*
Population Count	231	915
% Growth (12 years)		296.1
Annual % Growth (Compound)		12.2
% Share of Total G. A. Fleet	0.4	0.8

*SPEAS estimate of 1967 "eligible" fleet, unadjusted for "active" fleet determination, as shown in 1968 report.

There has been a fairly uniform growth rate, reflecting the interest of sport type activity; however, the actual number of aircraft is limited. It is not expected that this category of aircraft will show much growth in the future. The projected values are as follows:

	1967*	1975	1980
Population Count	1,152	1,700	1,900
% Growth (13 years)			64.9
Annual % Growth (Compound)			3.9
% Share of Total G. A. Fleet	0.9	0.9	0.7

*Values adjusted for "Active Fleet" determination.

(Figures 24, 25, 26, 26a, 26b, 27, 28, 29 and 30 follow)

Figure 24

GENERAL AVIATION
ACTIVE FLEET POPULATION
(ROTORCRAFT AND "OTHER")

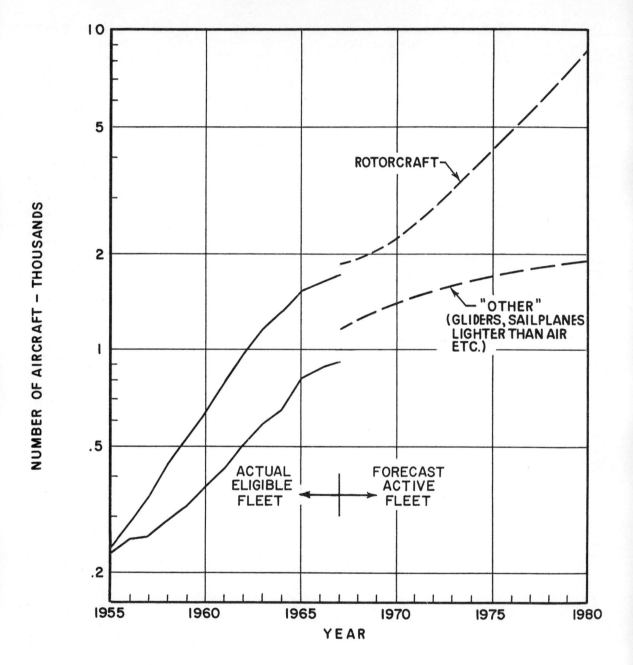

SOURCE: SPEAS ANALYSIS

Figure 25

45

ANNUAL PERCENTAGE GROWTH RATE OF ACTIVE FLEET
BY TYPE OF AIRCRAFT
ROTORCRAFT AND "OTHER"

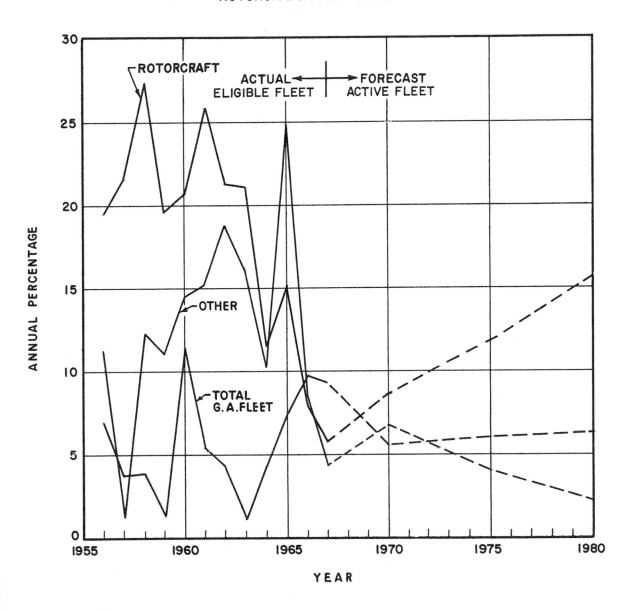

SOURCE: SPEAS ANALYSIS

Figure 26

GENERAL AVIATION AIRCRAFT
POPULATION OF ELIGIBLE AND ACTIVE FLEET
— ACTUAL AND FORECAST —

| | Single Engine Recip. | | Multi-Engine, Reciprocating | | | | Multi & Single Engine Turbine | | | | | | | |
| | | | To 12,500 lbs. | | Over 12,500 lbs. | | Turboprop Under 12,500 lbs. | Turboprop Over 12,500 lbs. | Pure Jet | | | | | Yearly |
	1-3 Place	4+ Place	To 600 hp	Over 600 hp		Total				Total	Rotor	Other	Total	Change
1955	35,740	19,240				3,342					237	231	58,790	—
1956	35,358	22,805				4,183					283	257	62,886	4,096
1957	35,898	23,751				5,036					344	260	65,289	2,403
1958	35,522	26,170				5,416					439	292	67,839	2,550
1959	34,543	27,301				6,034					525	324	68,727	888
1960	33,472	34,829				7,243					634	371	76,549	7,822
1961	32,800	38,206				8,241				160	798	427	80,632	4,083
1962	32,341	41,120				8,973				213	967	507	84,121	3,489
1963	30,977	42,657				9,450				245	1,171	588	85,088	967
1964	30,367	45,777				10,338				306	1,306	648	88,742	3,654
1965	31,364	49,789				11,403				574	1,503	809	95,442	6,700
1966	35,681	52,940				12,671				915	1,622	877	104,706	9,264
*1967	39,010	57,887				13,842				1,030	1,716	915	114,400	9,694
**1967	41,760	61,319	10,423	2,864	1,222	14,509	475	323	787	1,585	1,875	1,152	122,200	—
1975	55,400	98,200	19,500	6,200	800	26,500	2,400	1,000	2,600	6,000	4,200	1,700	192,000	9,680
1980	58,700	143,900	26,000	8,700	500	35,200	4,800	1,900	4,900	11,600	8,700	1,900	260,000	13,600

*Figures shown are SPEAS projection of FAA "eligible" values based on FAA 1966 percentages. Data as reproduced in original 1968 report.

**Values as developed by SPEAS for the 1967 active fleet.

Source: FAA historical data through 1966 (FAA "eligible" aircraft) and SPEAS development and projection of active aircraft for 1967 and subsequent years.

Figure 26a

GENERAL AVIATION ACTIVE FLEET POPULATION
TOTAL

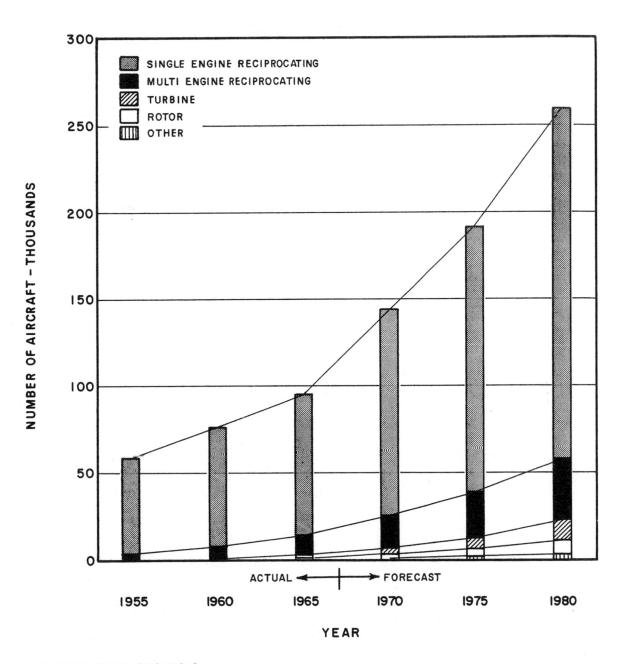

SOURCE: SPEAS ANALYSIS

Figure 26b

GENERAL AVIATION ACTIVE FLEET POPULATION
BY TYPE OF AIRCRAFT

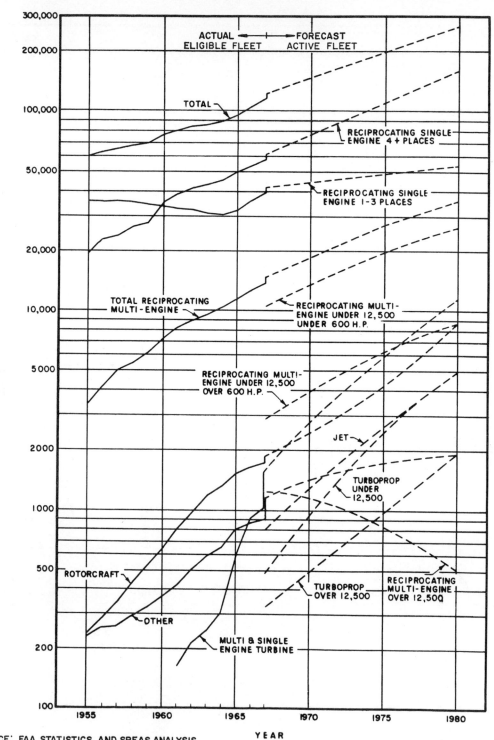

SOURCE: FAA STATISTICS AND SPEAS ANALYSIS

Figure 27

GENERAL AVIATION AIRCRAFT

ANNUAL PERCENTAGE GROWTH OF ELIGIBLE AND ACTIVE FLEET

— ACTUAL AND FORECAST —

| | Single Engine Recip. | | Multi-Engine Reciprocating | | | | Multi & Single Engine Turbine Turboprop | | | | Rotor | Other | Total |
| | | | To 12,500 lbs. | | Over 12,500 lbs. | | Under 12,500 lbs. | Over 12,500 lbs. | | | | | |
	1-3 Place	4+ Place	To 600 hp	Over 600 hp		Total			Pure Jet	Total			
1955													
1956	(1.1)	18.5				25.2					19.4	11.3	7.0
1957	1.5	4.1				20.4					21.6	1.2	3.8
1958	(1.0)	10.2				7.5					27.6	12.3	3.9
1959	(2.8)	4.3				11.4					19.6	11.0	1.3
1960	(3.1)	27.6				20.0					20.8	14.5	11.4
1961	(2.0)	9.7				13.8					25.9	15.1	5.3
1962	(1.4)	7.6				8.9				33.1	21.2	18.7	4.3
1963	(4.2)	3.7				5.3				15.0	21.1	16.0	1.1
1964	(2.0)	7.3				9.4				24.9	11.5	10.2	4.3
1965	3.3	8.8				10.3				87.6	15.1	24.8	7.5
1966	13.8	6.3				11.1				59.4	7.9	8.4	9.7
*1967	9.3	9.3				9.2				12.6	5.8	4.3	9.3
**1967	17.0	15.8				14.5				73.2	15.6	31.4	16.7
1975	3.2	6.1	8.2	10.1	(3.9)	7.8	22.0	15.1	16.1	18.1	10.6	5.0	5.8
1980	1.1	7.9	5.9	7.0	(9.0)	5.8	14.9	13.7	13.5	14.1	15.7	2.2	6.3

Note: The values for 1975 and 1980 are compound annual rates for the respective time intervals.

*Figures shown are based upon SPEAS projection of FAA 1966 values, as reproduced in original 1968 report.

**Based on population values as developed by SPEAS for the 1967 active fleet.

Source: SPEAS calculations, Figure 2.

Figure 28

GENERAL AVIATION AIRCRAFT

SHARE OF THE MARKET COMPOSITION OF THE ELIGIBLE & ACTIVE FLEET
— ACTUAL AND FORECAST —

	Single Engine Recip. 1-3 Place	4+ Place	Multi-Engine Reciprocating To 12,500 lbs. To 600 hp	Over 600 hp	Over 12,500 lbs.	Total	Multi & Single Engine Turbine Turboprop Under 12,500 lbs.	Over 12,500 lbs.	Pure Jet	Total	Rotor	Other	Total
1955	60.8	32.7				5.7					.4	.4	100%
1956	56.2	36.3				6.7					.4	.4	100
1957	55.0	36.4				7.7					.5	.4	100
1958	52.4	38.6				8.0					.6	.4	100
1959	50.2	39.7				8.8					.8	.5	100
1960	43.7	45.5				9.5					.8	.5	100
1961	40.7	47.4				10.2				.2	1.0	.5	100
1962	38.4	48.9				10.7				.3	1.1	.6	100
1963	36.4	50.1				11.1				.3	1.4	.7	100
1964	34.2	51.6				11.7				.3	1.5	.7	100
1965	32.9	52.2				11.9				.6	1.6	.8	100
1966	34.1	50.6				12.1				.9	1.5	.8	100
*1967	34.1	50.6				12.1				.9	1.5	.8	100
**1967	34.2	50.2	8.5	2.4	1.0	11.9	.4	.3	.6	1.3	1.5	.9	100
1975	28.9	51.1	10.2	3.2	.4	13.8	1.2	.5	1.4	3.1	2.2	.9	100
1980	22.6	55.3	10.0	3.3	.2	13.5	1.9	.7	1.9	4.5	3.4	.7	100

*1967 percentages are based on 1966 percentages relating to FAA "eligible" fleet distribution. Data shown are estimates as used in original 1968 report.

**Based on population values as developed by SPEAS for the 1967 "active" fleet.

Source: SPEAS Analysis.

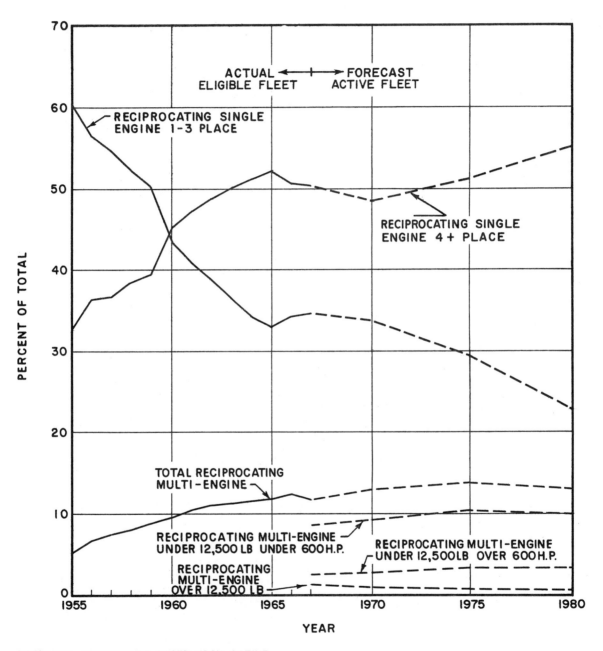

Figure 29

51

PERCENTAGE COMPOSITION OF TOTAL FLEET POPULATION

NOTE: 1967 VALUES ARE BASED UPON ACTIVE
FLEET TOTAL OF 122,200

SOURCE: SPEAS ANALYSIS

Figure 30

PERCENTAGE COMPOSITION OF TOTAL FLEET POPULATION

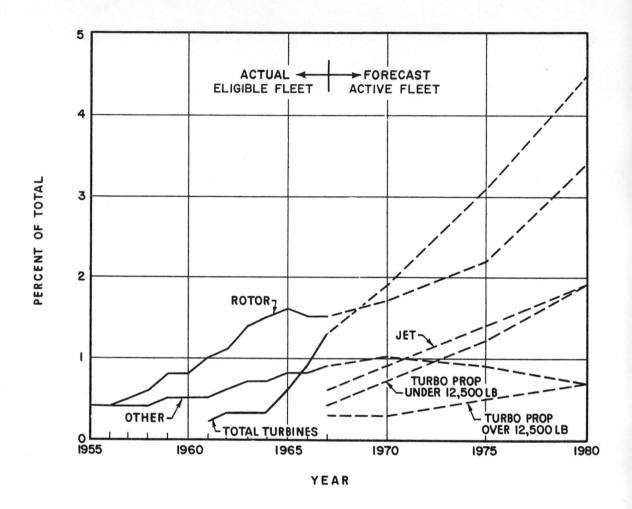

NOTE: 1967 VALUES ARE BASED UPON ACTIVE
FLEET TOTAL OF 122,200

SOURCE: SPEAS ANALYSIS

2. *Distribution of the Fleet by Category of Aircraft, by State and SMSA*

The history from 1957 through 1967 of the distribution of aircraft by category within each state and SMSA was determined from analysis of the FAA annual publication entitled "Census of U.S. Civil Aircraft." The FAA Aircraft Master Register as of March 31, 1969 was analyzed to determine 1968 values.

Rates of average change in percentage of the fleet in the individual states and SMSAs were then applied to the 1967 base year percentages to determine the mix of the area fleets for the forecast years, and these were applied to the previously determined total forecast populations of aircraft by state and SMSA. The summation of these values was confirmed by comparison with the previously forecast distribution of the total fleet.

An analysis of the distribution of the registered ownership of these aircraft for 1967 and 1968 by category and by state is presented in Figure 32, and by the top 75 SMSAs in Figure 34. As would be expected, California dominates the states not only in total aircraft but also in five of the categories. Texas, which has the second highest number of total aircraft, leads in the over 600 hp under 12,500 pounds and the over 12,500 pounds reciprocating categories. New York, virtually tied with Michigan for fourth ranking in total aircraft, leads in the turboprop and turbojet categories; this circum-

stance unquestionably arises from the concentration of industrial and financial interests in New York City, with registered addresses showing the headquarters city. Illinois ranks third in the numbers of total aircraft. The forecast by state is shown in Figure 33.

In the SMSAs, Los Angeles has the highest number of total aircraft and also dominates all categories except the turboprops and turbojets, which again appear in New York. The Chicago SMSA is second in total, and New York third, closely followed by San Francisco. The proportion of the total fleet represented by those registered in the top 75 SMSAs was constant at 44.4 percent in 1967 and 1968, but there is a slight shift towards the SMSAs in the turboprop and turbojet categories from 1967 to 1968. The forecast by SMSA is given in Figure 35.

Figure 31 presents a summary for reference, by category, showing that the total population has grown from 122,200 at the end of 1967 to 130,000 as of December 31, 1968, an increase of 6.4 percent. It can be seen that the largest absolute growth occurred in the single engine categories, although their percentage growth was below that of the fleet. The largest percentage increase (48.3 percent) was obtained in the small turboprop category, with turbojets and rotorcraft also experiencing significantly strong growth rates of 20.6 percent and 15.7 percent respectively.

(Figures 31, 32, 33, 34 and 35 follow)

Figure 31

ACTIVE AIRCRAFT POPULATION
1967 AND 1968 TOTALS FOR THE UNITED STATES
BY AIRCRAFT CATEGORY
AS OF DECEMBER 31

	1967	1968
Single Engine Reciprocating 1-3 Place	41,683	44,271
Single Engine Reciprocating 4 Places and Over	61,124	64,259
Multi Engine Reciprocating Up to 600 hp	10,359	11,325
Multi Engine Reciprocating Over 600 hp to 12,500 lbs	2,846	3,037
Multi Engine Reciprocating Over 12,500 lbs	1,215	1,180
Multi Engine Turboprop Up to 12,500 lbs	472	700
Multi Engine Turboprop Over 12,500 lbs	311	319
Multi Engine Turbojet	782	943
Rotorcraft	1,858	2,149
Other	1,150	1,317
Total United States	121,800	129,500
Outside United States	400	500
Grand Total	122,200	130,000

Source: FAA data and
        SPEAS Analysis.

Figure 32

ACTIVE AIRCRAFT POPULATION

DISTRIBUTION OF 1967 AND 1968 FLEETS BY CATEGORY BY STATE

State	Year	SE 1-3	SE 4+	ME 600-	ME 600+	ME 12.5+	ME 12.5—T	ME 12.5+T	T/J	Rotor	Other	Total
Alabama	1967	589	758	179	26	19	6	1	7	8	7	1,600
	1968	814	637	149	25	18	4	·	11	5	10	1,670
Alaska	1967	848	846	40	18	8	5	0	0	49	1	1,815
	1968	942	933	55	20	9	9	0	2	78	2	2,100
Arizona	1967	636	984	142	42	30	1	0	5	39	21	1,900
	1968	664	1,095	155	36	26	1	0	2	61	20	2,060
Arkansas	1967	666	740	174	49	11	5	0	4	5	1	1,635
	1968	712	774	178	49	8	8	0	7	0	4	1,740
California	1967	5,515	8,631	1,168	278	148	38	15	89	339	269	16,490
	1968	5,889	8,944	1,267	276	151	57	18	95	385	323	17,405
Colorado	1967	653	1,078	175	36	6	6	4	10	17	35	2,020
	1968	687	1,161	181	44	9	9	5	20	33	31	2,180
Connecticut	1967	364	524	89	17	4	7	0	7	24	19	1,055
	1968	388	548	106	16	4	10	0	5	21	22	1,120
Delaware	1967	130	226	59	29	2	7	4	25	4	4	490
	1968	137	243	76	31	3	17	7	31	5	5	555
District of Columbia	1967	53	345	45	56	101	4	18	11	24	28	685
	1968	53	371	53	57	93	9	19	13	22	30	720
Florida*	1967	1,644	2,093	540	157	123	13	4	22	87	27	4,710
	1968	1,696	2,232	572	160	116	24	3	12	108	37	4,960
Georgia	1967	870	1,100	256	61	13	7	6	13	14	10	2,350
	1968	958	1,234	291	64	9	14	3	16	16	10	2,615
Hawaii	1967	63	54	26	8	6	2	0	2	7	7	175
	1968	75	59	23	10	3	0	0	1	7	8	190
Idaho	1967	375	619	46	17	4	0	0	3	28	8	1,100
	1968	399	617	58	16	1	1	0	5	32	11	1,140
Illinois	1967	1,602	2,899	541	136	39	24	14	46	51	33	5,385
	1968	1,691	3,031	537	135	39	38	19	48	61	36	5,635
Indiana	1967	900	1,782	334	91	24	11	7	10	29	17	3,205
	1968	979	1,781	359	99	30	17	7	11	32	15	3,330
Iowa	1967	760	1,406	222	41	2	4	0	0	12	8	2,455
	1968	793	1,434	214	57	1	7	0	4	18	12	2,540

(Continued on Next Page)

Figure 32

(Continued from Preceding Page)

State	Year	SE 1-3	SE 4+	ME 600−	ME 600+	ME 12.5+	ME 12.5−	ME 12.5+T	T/J	Rotor	Other	Total
Kansas*	1967	916	1,547	231	51	8	11	0	16	18	22	2,820
	1968	934	1,671	240	58	10	13	0	19	21	24	2,990
Kentucky	1967	286	442	94	30	6	4	1	5	11	6	885
	1968	332	469	123	31	8	4	1	7	8	2	985
Louisiana	1967	807	776	185	53	22	3	5	5	154	0	2,010
	1968	838	849	196	57	22	5	3	5	170	0	2,145
Maine	1967	272	210	40	1	0	0	0	0	5	2	530
	1968	288	231	46	1	0	1	0	0	8	0	575
Maryland	1967	506	638	91	29	13	6	16	11	45	25	1,380
	1968	534	737	120	39	10	9	11	9	35	21	1,525
Massachusetts	1967	587	748	148	29	5	10	2	24	28	34	1,615
	1968	680	810	158	35	5	13	5	31	28	35	1,800
Michigan	1967	1,515	2,670	437	143	26	26	22	13	33	30	4,915
	1968	1,602	2,800	463	155	24	32	21	18	35	40	5,190
Minnesota	1967	1,349	1,557	169	43	11	8	13	24	31	10	3,215
	1968	1,428	1,638	182	51	12	10	12	27	33	17	3,410
Mississippi	1967	635	587	116	31	8	1	1	0	8	13	1,400
	1968	656	602	125	39	4	8	0	6	9	11	1,460
Missouri	1967	984	1,554	276	79	30	6	7	41	26	17	3,020
	1968	1,053	1,644	289	103	32	17	2	48	29	18	3,240
Montana	1967	565	777	88	16	7	4	0	1	17	0	1,475
	1968	575	799	83	19	5	2	0	1	26	0	1,510
Nebraska	1967	659	822	126	26	8	1	1	14	20	8	1,685
	1968	691	849	148	29	8	1	2	17	26	4	1,775
Nevada	1967	290	469	82	17	23	7	1	6	32	13	940
	1968	270	536	92	23	22	4	0	10	12	16	985
New Hampshire	1967	134	186	26	5	1	1	0	0	0	2	355
	1968	137	188	32	4	4	1	0	4	3	2	375
New Jersey	1967	878	1,362	251	45	12	7	11	22	34	28	2,650
	1968	960	1,397	267	39	11	18	12	30	43	33	2,810
New Mexico	1967	291	787	116	10	5	8	1	0	7	13	1,230
	1968	276	816	133	20	6	0	1	0	14	24	1,290
New York	1967	1,700	2,247	406	128	76	61	62	122	83	95	4,980
	1968	1,787	2,409	454	132	71	91	65	138	96	102	5,345
North Carolina	1967	714	1,098	217	47	8	11	3	5	23	14	2,140
	1968	729	1,134	248	58	10	19	3	8	21	15	2,245

(Continued on Next Page)

Figure 32
(Continued from Preceding Page)

State	Year	SE 1-3	SE 4+	ME 600—	ME 600+	ME 12.5+	ME 12.5—T	ME 12.5+T	T/J	Rotor	Other	Total
North Dakota	1967	580	389	30	2	0	0	0	1	1	2	1,005
	1968	590	397	37	7	1	0	0	0	1	2	1,035
Ohio	1967	1,644	2,712	486	157	45	36	25	60	58	64	5,290
	1968	1,725	2,780	556	171	43	54	26	76	63	62	5,560
Oklahoma*	1967	839	1,272	199	83	17	25	6	23	49	7	2,520
	1968	1,022	1,385	263	87	21	24	4	26	48	5	2,885
Oregon	1967	807	1,420	205	67	19	2	1	2	89	8	2,620
	1968	836	1,462	186	66	13	2	1	4	104	6	2,680
Pennsylvania*	1967	1,301	1,875	394	94	46	24	19	44	72	49	3,920
	1968	1,333	2,024	427	102	42	40	21	58	80	61	4,190
Rhode Island	1967	64	91	14	4	1	1	0	0	10	0	185
	1968	69	114	19	4	0	2	0	2	10	0	220
South Carolina	1967	332	442	113	33	15	5	0	2	23	10	975
	1968	373	458	124	32	10	7	0	5	30	16	1,065
South Dakota	1967	454	424	39	8	3	0	0	0	2	5	935
	1968	415	424	33	7	2	0	0	0	3	1	885
Tennessee	1967	487	828	251	63	17	11	0	12	11	10	1,690
	1968	509	862	244	58	19	14	1	15	13	15	1,750
Texas*	1967	3,202	4,587	897	306	190	44	28	46	124	81	9,505
	1968	3,304	4,713	1,029	321	191	53	28	64	147	95	9,945
Utah	1967	214	432	53	14	5	0	0	1	13	3	735
	1968	195	467	67	16	0	0	0	1	17	7	770
Vermont	1967	95	103	36	7	0	1	0	1	0	17	260
	1968	97	114	31	18	0	2	0	2	0	14	280
Virginia	1967	560	781	128	34	2	4	4	4	10	18	1,545
	1968	620	841	147	42	4	5	2	4	17	28	1,710
Washington	1967	1,072	1,503	124	24	7	5	1	13	57	34	2,840
	1968	1,200	1,701	168	24	5	7	0	8	74	43	3,230
West Virginia	1967	148	271	51	19	0	0	0	1	5	5	500
	1968	160	309	73	21	1	2	0	1	7	6	580
Wisconsin	1967	914	1,101	193	75	19	6	2	8	12	10	2,340
	1968	965	1,146	219	63	20	14	4	15	19	14	2,480
Wyoming	1967	214	332	31	11	20	0	1	1	10	0	620
	1968	211	333	29	10	22	1	1	1	10	2	620
Total	1967	41,683	61,124	10,359	2,846	1,215	472	311	782	1,858	1,150	121,800
	1968	44,271	64,259	11,325	3,037	1,180	700	319	943	2,149	1,317	129,500

*Figures include units registered to local aircraft manufacturers at time of report.
These units were then either awaiting customer delivery, or were being operated for company transportation or engineering purposes.
Source: SPEAS Analysis.

Figure 33
ACTIVE AIRCRAFT POPULATION
FORECAST OF DISTRIBUTION BY CATEGORY BY STATE

State	Year	Multi-Engine	Single Engine 4+ Places	Rotor-craft	Other	Total
Alabama	1975	436	1,063	33	769	2,300
	1980	621	1,504	73	803	3,000
Alaska	1975	89	1,120	97	1,095	2,400
	1980	131	1,369	164	1,135	2,800
Arizona	1975	429	1,449	72	751	2,700
	1980	544	1,779	121	656	3,100
Arkansas	1975	547	1,312	34	1,008	2,900
	1980	825	1,969	84	1,122	4,000
California	1975	3,372	13,377	631	7,520	24,900
	1980	4,758	19,873	1,269	7,901	33,800
Colorado	1975	453	1,734	48	865	3,100
	1980	593	2,365	100	842	3,900
Connecticut	1975	241	811	50	498	1,600
	1980	329	1,160	93	517	2,100
Delaware	1975	266	367	12	154	800
	1980	387	541	28	144	1,100
Dist. Columbia	1975	326	679	41	53	1,100
	1980	410	846	76	69	1,400
Florida	1975	1,699	3,331	188	2,282	7,500
	1980	2,550	5,055	392	2,503	10,500
Georgia	1975	850	2,071	62	1,318	4,300
	1980	1,373	3,331	156	1,540	6,400
Hawaii	1975	96	89	12	103	300
	1980	206	197	32	165	600
Idaho	1975	150	984	49	516	1,700
	1980	209	1,375	93	523	2,200
Illinois	1975	1,626	4,732	145	2,098	8,600
	1980	2,481	7,114	330	2,174	12,100
Indiana	1975	1,028	2,778	92	1,102	5,000
	1980	1,524	4,089	201	1,085	6,900
Iowa	1975	478	1,738	44	839	3,100
	1980	788	2,758	111	943	4,600
Kansas	1975	589	2,379	55	1,177	4,200
	1980	806	3,376	125	1,192	5,500
Kentucky	1975	282	630	15	373	1,300
	1980	425	916	29	430	1,800
Louisiana	1975	579	1,417	225	1,179	3,400
	1980	842	2,202	417	1,339	4,800
Maine	1975	97	321	16	366	800
	1980	141	442	31	386	1,000
Maryland	1975	537	1,803	129	1,231	3,700
	1980	922	3,250	300	1,627	6,100
Massachusetts	1975	470	1,198	60	871	2,600
	1980	693	1,747	123	937	3,500
Michigan	1975	1,193	3,951	120	1,836	7,100
	1980	1,579	5,485	250	1,786	9,100
Minnesota	1975	512	2,387	81	1,820	4,800
	1980	718	3,440	174	1,969	6,300
Mississippi	1975	378	936	17	769	2,100
	1980	571	1,400	35	795	2,800
Missouri	1975	879	2,526	78	1,318	4,800
	1980	1,298	3,670	173	1,359	6,500
Montana	1975	224	1,200	41	735	2,200
	1980	315	1,721	87	777	2,900

(Continued on Next Page)

Figure 33
(Continued from Preceding Page)

State	Year	Multi-Engine	Single Engine 4+ Places	Rotor-craft	Other	Total
Nebraska	1975	390	1,281	47	883	2,600
	1980	587	1,862	100	951	3,500
Nevada	1975	262	787	71	381	1,500
	1980	358	1,135	127	380	2,000
New Hampshire	1975	77	296	8	219	600
	1980	109	433	19	239	800
New Jersey	1975	864	2,720	109	1,507	5,200
	1980	1,307	4,327	246	1,720	7,600
New Mexico	1975	275	1,235	25	365	1,900
	1980	360	1,668	56	317	2,400
New York	1975	1,846	4,090	195	2,669	8,800
	1980	2,628	6,230	413	2,929	12,200
North Carolina	1975	733	1,875	74	1,119	3,800
	1980	1,131	2,871	165	1,233	5,400
North Dakota	1975	83	712	17	888	1,700
	1980	138	1,127	46	1,089	2,400
Ohio	1975	1,470	3,976	148	2,006	7,600
	1980	1,887	5,406	289	1,917	9,500
Oklahoma	1975	712	2,027	94	1,167	4,000
	1980	936	2,819	181	1,164	5,100
Oregon	1975	518	2,090	122	969	3,700
	1980	699	2,925	225	951	4,800
Pennsylvania	1975	1,373	3,025	161	1,741	6,300
	1980	1,964	4,345	318	1,773	8,400
Rhode Island	1975	40	149	15	96	300
	1980	56	216	27	101	400
South Carolina	1975	440	993	56	611	2,100
	1980	745	1,683	130	742	3,300
South Dakota	1975	122	808	19	751	1,700
	1980	184	1,209	47	860	2,300
Tennessee	1975	652	1,150	37	562	2,400
	1980	963	1,695	84	558	3,300
Texas	1975	2,751	7,246	276	4,127	14,400
	1980	3,775	10,551	579	4,295	19,200
Utah	1975	225	868	36	371	1,500
	1980	366	1,355	79	400	2,200
Vermont	1975	100	158	4	138	400
	1980	136	216	9	139	500
Virginia	1975	377	1,333	53	837	2,600
	1980	576	2,127	121	977	3,800
Washington	1975	339	2,121	95	1,346	3,900
	1980	451	2,920	185	1,344	4,900
West Virginia	1975	162	433	18	187	800
	1980	239	636	37	187	1,100
Wisconsin	1975	538	1,629	57	1,176	3,400
	1980	692	2,212	115	1,181	4,200
Wyoming	1975	125	417	18	241	800
	1980	173	560	34	234	1,000
Total U.S.	1975	32,300	97,800	4,200	57,000	191,300
	1980	46,500	143,500	8,700	60,400	259,100
Outside U.S.	1975	200	400	—	100	700
	1980	300	400	—	200	900
GRAND TOTAL	1975	32,500	98,200	4,200	57,100	192,000
	1980	46,800	143,900	8,700	60,600	260,000

Note: Totals may not add due to rounding.
Source: SPEAS Analysis.

Figure 34

ACTIVE AIRCRAFT POPULATION

DISTRIBUTION OF 1967 AND 1968 FLEETS BY CATEGORY BY SMSA

SMSA Area	Year	SE 1-3	SE 4+	ME 600—	ME 600+	ME 12.5+	ME 12.5—T	ME 12.5+T	T/J	Rotor	Other	Total
New York	1967	614	977	229	64	66	30	46	108	40	22	2,196
	1968	652	1,064	261	75	34	67	52	123	56	31	2,415
Chicago	1967	749	1,600	331	66	23	8	13	34	35	24	2,883
	1968	775	1,581	340	70	17	24	7	39	37	19	2,909
Los Angeles	1967	1,351	2,361	358	116	94	18	6	43	160	89	4,596
	1968	1,464	2,365	387	128	84	35	6	60	174	105	4,813
Philadelphia	1967	427	657	116	34	24	11	8	12	39	20	1,348
	1968	484	730	125	35	18	17	7	12	40	19	1,487
Detroit	1967	425	988	189	67	14	13	11	6	16	17	1,746
	1968	452	1,019	204	69	12	13	10	10	14	18	1,821
Boston	1967	299	393	77	16	5	7	2	22	18	26	865
	1968	355	413	84	21	4	11	4	28	16	22	958
San Francisco	1967	690	1,020	172	54	22	5	2	13	19	40	2,037
	1968	657	1,098	155	40	11	9	4	16	31	64	2,085
Pittsburgh	1967	246	341	58	11	11	8	8	18	12	6	719
	1968	250	395	68	20	12	13	11	26	11	11	816
St. Louis	1967	327	507	119	39	11	2	6	26	11	18	1,067
	1968	330	513	90	68	11	8	2	37	9	9	1,077
Washington, D.C.	1967	367	753	107	59	105	4	18	11	39	44	1,507
	1968	407	898	134	72	99	9	19	13	35	52	1,738
Cleveland	1967	202	444	77	28	6	7	5	6	10	7	792
	1968	225	429	106	40	7	10	3	10	13	6	849
Baltimore	1967	226	278	40	19	4	2	1	11	8	9	598
	1968	214	287	43	24	2	4	2	9	7	7	598
Newark	1967	191	321	63	6	1	1	2	5	7	9	606
	1968	177	334	72	6	0	6	2	10	13	10	630
Minneapolis	1967	510	723	108	30	10	5	8	21	17	7	1,439
	1968	530	755	114	33	11	7	10	22	19	9	1,510
Houston	1967	483	679	140	73	52	8	14	12	20	20	1,501
	1968	409	687	167	53	52	16	11	16	31	13	1,455

(Continued on Next Page)

Figure 34

(Continued from Preceding Page)

SMSA Area	Year	SE 1-3	SE 4+	ME 600-	ME 600+	ME 12.5+	ME 12.5-	ME 12.5+T	T/J	Rotor	Other	Total
Buffalo	1967	116	141	19	4	1	1	1	1	6	4	294
	1968	137	138	28	6	6	1	1	2	8	2	329
Milwaukee	1967	215	319	67	23	8	1	2	2	8	10	655
	1968	224	355	74	20	8	4	3	3	8	10	709
Cincinnati	1967	114	213	53	18	5	1	5	2	5	10	426
	1968	133	197	54	20	6	1	4	9	7	9	440
Paterson	1967	136	306	70	13	0	0	2	5	2	7	541
	1968	155	304	88	18	3	3	3	7	3	7	591
Dallas	1967	395	677	175	53	49	5	2	12	7	15	1,390
	1968	403	729	197	57	37	7	3	17	9	27	1,486
Seattle	1967	424	573	58	8	4	0	1	13	17	24	1,122
	1968	462	701	84	9	0	1	0	8	31	29	1,325
Kansas City	1967	336	577	111	20	17	4	1	5	10	7	1,088
	1968	383	619	139	23	1	4	0	4	16	7	1,196
San Diego	1967	306	527	89	17	5	0	1	2	11	24	982
	1968	298	577	113	12	3	0	2	10	19	27	1,061
Atlanta	1967	341	540	124	36	12	1	6	12	8	7	1,087
	1968	356	539	128	35	8	3	3	14	9	6	1,151
Indianapolis	1967	209	449	90	28	6	4	6	2	5	5	804
	1968	212	438	98	26	12	1	3	2	6	6	804
Miami	1967	413	344	106	51	58	1	4	13	13	6	1,009
	1968	423	355	124	48	48	2	1	7	22	9	1,039
Denver	1967	306	535	112	28	6	6	4	8	12	6	1,023
	1968	326	540	121	34	9	8	6	19	28	11	1,102
New Orleans	1967	94	147	45	11	4	0	2	2	98	0	403
	1968	92	146	45	10	11	2	2	2	100	0	410
Portland	1967	326	607	119	49	4	2	1	2	23	3	1,136
	1968	348	598	98	41	4	1	1	3	41	6	1,141
San Bernardino	1967	373	530	71	11	4	0	0	0	19	21	1,029
	1968	380	562	63	16	4	1	0	1	20	24	1,071
Tampa	1967	128	236	58	11	7	0	0	2	8	1	451
	1968	128	240	57	7	7	0	0	0	12	1	452
Columbus	1967	143	266	58	17	13	2	1	6	12	9	527
	1968	138	280	71	18	9	7	1	17	9	9	559
Rochester	1967	114	184	18	11	2	2	2	0	0	11	344
	1968	122	195	23	11	2	0	3	0	2	8	364

(Continued on Next Page)

Figure 34

(Continued from Preceding Page)

SMSA Area	Year	SE 1-3	SE 4+	ME 600-	ME 600+	ME 12.5+	ME 12.5-T	ME 12.5+T	T/J	Rotor	Other	Total
Dayton	1967	165	243	41	9	1	2	2	1	6	7	477
	1968	189	304	49	11	4	2	3	2	7	9	580
Louisville	1967	83	112	40	5	2	1	1	1	4	3	252
	1968	80	124	47	7	1	1	1	1	1	1	264
Birmingham	1967	52	141	55	12	2	4	1	1	0	0	267
	1968	43	138	54	10	1	3	0	2	0	0	251
Providence	1967	45	61	8	2	1	0	0	0	10	1	128
	1968	48	82	8	3	0	0	0	0	10	0	151
San Antonio	1967	106	217	88	31	12	4	2	0	8	5	473
	1968	122	186	90	34	8	2	1	1	8	6	458
Anaheim	1967	287	553	75	8	7	1	2	1	14	37	985
	1968	346	622	91	9	9	2	0	1	23	37	1,140
Hartford	1967	90	141	30	6	1	4	0	4	8	3	287
	1968	91	152	32	7	3	3	0	3	4	3	298
Memphis	1967	164	280	82	24	5	6	0	6	5	4	576
	1968	161	278	77	27	8	8	1	8	6	0	574
Phoenix	1967	354	488	71	25	20	1	0	5	33	13	1,010
	1968	385	552	94	26	22	1	0	2	44	16	1,142
New Haven	1967	55	76	11	6	1	0	0	1	11	0	161
	1968	62	83	22	3	0	0	0	2	8	2	182
Albany	1967	87	111	17	7	1	1	1	0	1	6	232
	1968	119	119	14	2	2	2	0	0	4	4	266
Bridgeport	1967	79	153	25	4	0	0	0	2	4	7	274
	1968	97	181	35	4	1	2	0	1	8	6	335
San Jose	1967	361	602	78	14	0	1	0	0	5	15	1,076
	1968	363	626	89	17	0	3	0	0	6	17	1,121
Toledo	1967	83	187	41	13	2	2	5	7	4	1	345
	1968	88	193	32	13	2	4	6	6	1	5	350
Sacramento	1967	300	375	45	6	0	0	0	0	2	7	735
	1968	295	437	34	2	0	0	0	0	7	11	786
Jersey City	1967	13	17	11	1	0	0	1	2	0	1	46
	1968	11	17	10	1	0	0	0	0	0	1	44
Akron	1967	84	167	23	12	11	1	3	5	2	2	314
	1968	94	184	28	14	7	3	2	8	6	7	352
Worcester	1967	81	105	14	3	0	0	3	1	4	5	211
	1968	89	111	16	3	0	0	0	2	6	3	234

(Continued on Next Page)

Figure 34

(Continued from Preceding Page)

SMSA Area	Year	SE 1-3	SE 4+	ME 600-	ME 600+	ME 12.5+	ME 12.5-T	ME 12.5+T	T/J	Rotor	Other	Total
Norfolk	1967	35	53	8	1	0	1	0	0	6	1	105
	1968	43	52	10	2	0	1	0	0	3	2	113
Gary	1967	54	125	11	1	1	1	0	0	1	1	195
	1968	71	151	28	3	1	1	4	0	1	0	256
Fort Worth	1967	264	377	54	18	10	2	4	0	36	9	774
	1968	316	414	73	20	11	2	1	3	49	7	896
Syracuse	1967	90	140	28	13	2	1	0	0	6	4	284
	1968	104	142	22	13	1	2	0	0	3	4	291
Springfield	1967	61	100	14	0	0	0	0	0	1	1	177
	1968	73	110	17	1	1	0	0	0	0	1	203
Greensboro	1967	119	216	45	10	1	6	2	2	1	2	404
	1968	115	238	45	11	1	8	2	2	2	2	426
Oklahoma City*	1967	157	346	84	35	7	19	0	13	7	5	673
	1968	179	375	100	31	10	17	1	14	4	2	732
Youngstown	1967	85	93	22	18	0	8	1	7	4	2	240
	1968	78	103	30	9	0	12	1	6	2	2	243
Honolulu	1967	62	43	19	9	3	0	0	1	6	6	149
	1968	67	46	21	10	3	0	0	1	6	6	160
Allentown	1967	61	83	7	5	1	0	2	4	0	0	163
	1968	66	97	12	3	3	0	2	8	1	1	193
Nashville	1967	51	98	42	16	11	4	0	6	4	5	237
	1968	58	96	38	8	4	7	0	4	3	6	224
Grand Rapids	1967	107	202	24	8	1	0	0	1	1	5	349
	1968	104	199	27	10	0	0	0	2	0	3	345
Omaha	1967	116	223	45	10	4	0	0	7	1	0	406
	1968	113	260	53	18	2	1	0	9	6	0	462
Jacksonville	1967	52	92	37	8	5	0	1	0	2	4	200
	1968	59	99	28	9	3	3	0	0	3	3	208
Salt Lake City	1967	95	200	28	7	4	0	0	1	7	6	348
	1968	76	204	43	11	0	0	0	1	7	6	348
Richmond	1967	65	89	24	8	0	1	0	1	1	1	190
	1968	45	86	24	10	0	3	0	1	1	2	172
Tulsa	1967	159	278	51	31	7	3	0	4	14	6	553
	1968	201	270	65	31	8	6	1	8	13	2	605
Flint	1967	122	181	20	8	1	0	0	0	1	2	335
	1968	116	196	19	8	0	0	0	0	1	2	343

(Continued on Next Page)

Figure 34

(Continued from Preceding Page)

SMSA Area	Year	SE 1-3	SE 4+	ME 600-	ME 600+	ME 12.5+	ME 12.5-T	ME 12.5+T	T/J	Rotor	Other	Total
Wilmington	1967	82	173	47	24	2	7	4	24	1	2	366
	1968	91	180	60	27	3	14	7	26	3	7	418
Wichita*	1967	232	464	105	35	5	7	0	10	4	6	868
	1968	200	522	89	37	6	12	0	11	9	15	901
Harrisburg	1967	59	90	29	8	1	0	0	0	2	5	194
	1968	64	89	26	8	1	0	0	0	3	6	197
Knoxville	1967	57	107	43	6	0	1	0	0	1	0	215
	1968	50	92	35	7	3	0	0	0	3	1	191
Fresno	1967	159	248	48	10	1	1	0	0	10	1	478
	1968	175	256	49	7	1	1	0	0	11	1	501
Mobile	1967	59	52	23	5	4	3	1	1	0	0	148
	1968	59	60	27	6	6	2	1	1	0	0	162
Total	1967	16,488	27,315	5,240	1,573	791	252	221	556	953	722	54,111
	1968	17,307	28,857	5,718	1,656	688	423	220	697	1,139	804	57,509

Note: Aircraft type abbreviations used are:

Reciprocating Engine

SE 1-3	Single Engine, 1-3 Place
SE 4+	Single Engine, 4 or more Places
ME 600-	Multi-Engine, to 12,500 lbs., to 600 HP
ME 600+	Multi-Engine, to 12,500 lbs., over 600 HP
ME 12.5+	Multi-Engine, over 12,500 lbs.

Turbine Engine

ME 12.5-T	Turboprop Single and Multi-Engine, to 12,500 lbs.
ME 12.5+T	Turboprop Single and Multi-Engine, over 12,500 lbs.
	Turbo-Jet
	Rotorcraft
	Unspecified or Other

*Figures include units registered to local aircraft manufacturers at time of report. These units were then either awaiting customer delivery, or were being operated for company transportation or engineering purposes.

Source: SPEAS Analysis.

Figure 35

ACTIVE AIRCRAFT POPULATION
FORECAST OF DISTRIBUTION BY CATEGORY BY SMSA

SMSA Area	Year	Multi-Engine	Single Engine 4+ Places	Rotor-craft	Other	Total
New York	1975	997	1,757	124	822	3,700
	1980	1,329	2,423	197	851	4,800
Chicago	1975	705	2,500	108	887	4,200
	1980	965	3,439	183	914	5,500
Los Angeles	1975	1,022	3,798	323	1,757	6,900
	1980	1,401	5,224	489	1,886	9,000
Philadelphia	1975	430	1,238	110	622	2,400
	1980	689	1,892	186	733	3,500
Detroit	1975	621	1,858	68	554	3,100
	1980	893	2,560	120	527	4,100
Boston	1975	238	675	48	439	1,400
	1980	357	963	79	501	1,900
San Francisco	1975	493	1,936	76	995	3,500
	1980	756	2,974	149	1,221	5,100
Pittsburgh	1975	215	615	39	331	1,200
	1980	269	817	63	350	1,500
St. Louis	1975	333	1,069	42	456	1,900
	1980	494	1,600	80	526	2,700
Washington, D.C.	1975	612	1,906	124	458	3,100
	1980	1,071	3,352	255	422	5,100
Cleveland	1975	236	765	37	262	1,300
	1980	321	1,052	61	266	1,700
Baltimore	1975	223	824	40	512	1,600
	1980	397	1,472	88	743	2,700
Newark	1975	134	574	34	258	1,000
	1980	174	789	57	281	1,300
Minneapolis	1975	352	1,426	68	754	2,600
	1980	515	2,082	121	882	3,600
Houston	1975	486	1,109	52	854	2,400
	1980	671	1,504	97	928	3,200
Buffalo	1975	49	258	22	171	500
	1980	59	329	32	180	600
Milwaukee	1975	203	635	30	332	1,200
	1980	300	951	55	394	1,700
Cincinnati	1975	169	354	16	161	700
	1980	214	414	22	150	800
Paterson	1975	225	716	19	239	1,200
	1980	410	1,316	49	324	2,100
Dallas	1975	460	1,219	54	467	2,200
	1980	690	1,935	114	561	3,300
Seattle	1975	139	1,027	47	587	1,800
	1980	212	1,502	84	702	2,500
Kansas City	1975	242	1,038	42	479	1,800
	1980	383	1,638	83	597	2,700
San Diego	1975	216	869	40	376	1,500
	1980	355	1,329	75	441	2,200
Atlanta	1975	376	1,103	41	480	2,000
	1980	699	1,960	94	647	3,400
Indianapolis	1975	260	844	30	266	1,400
	1980	387	1,193	55	266	1,900

(Continued on Next Page)

Figure 35
(Continued from Preceding Page)

SMSA Area	Year	Multi-Engine	Single Engine 4+ Places	Rotor-craft	Other	Total
Miami	1975	410	632	42	716	1,800
	1980	628	976	76	1,021	2,700
Denver	1975	251	849	35	365	1,500
	1980	314	1,073	55	357	1,800
New Orleans	1975	87	183	143	87	500
	1980	139	293	257	111	800
Portland	1975	285	1,026	69	420	1,800
	1980	448	1,619	124	508	2,700
San Bernadino	1975	135	845	47	473	1,500
	1980	196	1,187	77	541	2,000
Tampa	1975	161	422	23	194	800
	1980	294	701	45	260	1,300
Columbus	1975	254	582	35	229	1,100
	1980	423	942	67	269	1,700
Rochester	1975	84	395	11	210	700
	1980	141	653	25	281	1,100
Dayton	1975	103	501	28	267	900
	1980	149	766	54	331	1,300
Louisville	1975	90	192	11	107	400
	1980	153	295	20	132	600
Birmingham	1975	137	288	6	69	500
	1980	204	420	14	62	700
Providence	1975	19	104	17	60	200
	1980	20	110	19	51	200
San Antonio	1975	229	325	20	126	700
	1980	282	382	26	110	800
Anaheim	1975	252	1,329	62	558	2,200
	1980	427	2,182	128	762	3,500
Hartford	1975	76	265	21	139	500
	1980	121	450	41	188	800
Memphis	1975	250	513	17	220	1,000
	1980	440	840	36	284	1,600
Phoenix	1975	227	830	73	470	1,600
	1980	319	1,087	106	488	2,000
New Haven	1975	35	160	26	79	300
	1980	47	226	39	88	400
Albany	1975	72	248	10	169	500
	1980	130	418	22	230	800
Bridgeport	1975	74	296	19	110	500
	1980	99	371	27	102	600
San Jose	1975	200	1,194	57	649	2,100
	1980	342	1,984	113	861	3,300
Toledo	1975	117	283	9	90	500
	1980	176	414	18	91	700
Sacramento	1975	102	927	14	456	1,500
	1980	188	1,462	43	608	2,400
Jersey City	1975	35	38	1	27	100
	1980	37	39	1	22	100
Akron	1975	129	220	8	143	500
	1980	198	317	15	170	700
Worcester	1975	36	161	10	94	300
	1980	50	226	16	108	400
Norfolk	1975	28	116	12	43	200
	1980	30	125	14	30	200

(Continued on Next Page)

Figure 35
(Continued from Preceding Page)

SMSA Area	Year	Multi-Engine	Single Engine 4+ Places	Rotor-craft	Other	Total
Gary	1975	54	270	8	67	400
	1980	89	431	19	61	600
Fort Worth	1975	141	649	77	333	1,200
	1980	176	860	112	352	1,500
Syracuse	1975	90	261	17	132	500
	1980	118	328	25	129	600
Springfield	1975	34	234	6	126	400
	1980	42	309	13	136	500
Greensboro	1975	140	458	14	188	800
	1980	255	844	35	266	1,400
Oklahoma City	1975	253	541	22	184	1,000
	1980	365	799	41	195	1,400
Youngstown	1975	105	177	10	108	400
	1980	135	236	16	112	500
Honolulu	1975	53	59	10	78	200
	1980	86	92	17	105	300
Allentown	1975	39	170	4	87	300
	1980	69	299	10	122	500
Nashville	1975	138	166	11	85	400
	1980	222	256	19	103	600
Grand Rapids	1975	63	381	11	144	600
	1980	86	537	19	158	800
Omaha	1975	124	346	10	120	600
	1980	179	481	20	120	800
Jacksonville	1975	87	137	7	69	300
	1980	125	188	12	75	400
Salt Lake City	1975	87	354	18	141	600
	1980	127	481	33	159	800
Richmond	1975	90	195	9	105	400
	1980	146	308	19	128	600
Tulsa	1975	151	427	32	189	800
	1980	189	567	51	194	1,000
Flint	1975	56	287	8	150	500
	1980	90	419	16	175	700
Wilmington	1975	289	453	19	139	900
	1980	542	845	45	167	1,600
Wichita	1975	342	829	20	309	1,500
	1980	455	1,018	33	295	1,800
Harrisburg	1975	107	252	17	124	500
	1980	232	528	42	198	1,000
Knoxville	1975	59	100	4	37	200
	1980	97	154	7	42	300
Fresno	1975	109	384	21	185	700
	1980	139	459	30	172	800
Mobile	1975	80	103	2	115	300
	1980	145	178	6	170	500
SMSA Total	1975	16,007	50,270	2,817	23,206	92,300
	1980	24,116	74,985	5,005	26,993	131,100
Outside of SMSA's	1975	16,493	47,930	1,383	33,894	99,700
	1980	22,684	68,915	3,695	33,607	128,900
GRAND TOTAL	1975	32,500	98,200	4,200	57,100	192,000
	1980	46,800	143,900	8,700	60,600	260,000

Note: Totals may not add due to rounding.
Source: SPEAS Analysis.

CHAPTER FOUR

AIRCRAFT FLIGHT HOURS AND UTILIZATION

The forecasts of hours flown by the General Aviation fleet and average aircraft utilization were developed from an extensive data analysis of the FAA's Aircraft Registration Master File tapes.[1] This analysis allowed determination of utilization rates by category of aircraft for the country as a whole and for those states and SMSAs with significant numbers of reporting aircraft.

The utilization rates were applied to the active fleet population to determine total hours flown. These hours differ from the total recorded in the FAA tape for eligible aircraft, due to the fact that some 15-20 percent of the aircraft considered in this report as active aircraft show no hours at all. This segment includes all aircraft less than a year old which have not yet been inspected, aircraft on continuous maintenance, and aircraft with short ineligibilities. The new aircraft not yet inspected will be approximately one-half year old on average, and thus will have less than average utilization during the preceding calendar year. Those on continuous maintenance will have higher than average utilization, and those with temporary ineligibilities will be lower than average.

Active aircraft hours flown were developed in a number of different ways to obtain a perspective on how the population of the general aircraft fleet is actually being utilized. Among the values developed on an hourly basis were:

- Hours flown by use for the top 75 SMSA areas and a separate tabulation for areas not within the top 75 SMSAs.
- Hours flown by the ten separate General Aviation aircraft categories (as outlined in prior sections of this report), used in the top 75 SMSAs and other areas.

[1]Tapes analyzed were dated as of March 1968 and March 1969.

- Similar breakdown to the two foregoing items by the 50 states and the District of Columbia.
- Annual hourly utilization by aircraft type and by use for the top 75 SMSAs and other areas.
- Hourly utilization for the 50 states and the District of Columbia.
- Hourly utilization by manufacturers' make and model by use and by the ten type categories.
- Hourly blocks flown by use and by the ten type categories.

The data analyzed in the various areas just outlined enabled the construction of a substantial statistical base from which subsequent analyses could be prepared where, in the past, little or no published information existed.

After constructing a reasonable and logical statistical base, as outlined above, an analysis was made of historical data, as reported by the FAA, to ascertain past trends. Total General Aviation flight hours have shown a steady annual rate of growth until recently. The total number of flight hours recorded by the FAA has risen from 8.5 million hours in 1953 to 22.2 million in 1967. Between 1953 and 1965, the average annual rate of growth was 5.8 percent; however, following the sharp increase in flight hours from 16.7 to 21.0 million hours between 1965 and 1966, the average annual rate of increase has risen to 6.4 percent. The average aircraft annual utilization figure increased from 140 hours in 1953 to 194 hours in 1967, an average annual increase of 2.2 percent. Figure 36 shows the number of hours flown between 1953 and 1967. It should be borne in mind that the FAA figures are lower than the SPEAS figures by about 10 percent, reflecting factors already considered. Figure 37 shows the average annual utilization by aircraft type.

Figure 36

ESTIMATED HOURS FLOWN IN GENERAL AVIATION BY AIRCRAFT TYPE 1953-1967

Aircraft Type	Total Annual Hours Flown (in '000)									
	1953	1957	1960	1961	1962	1963	1964	1965	1966	1967
Single Engine 1-3 Place Recip.	5,050	4,966	4,017	4,207	3,966	4,060	4,166	4,521	5,847	7,337
Single Engine 4+ Place Recip.	2,628	4,145	5,771	6,598	6,659	7,777	8,055	8,506	10,335	10,189
Multi-Engine	803	1,707	2,189	2,430	2,436	2,720	2,876	2,999	3,858	3,450
Multi-Engine Turbine	—	—	—	65	94	109	137	191	423	548
Rotorcraft	39	105	207	264	256	387	447	450	492	538
Other	7	15	19	29	39	53	57	66	68	65
Total Hours All Types	8,527	10,938	12,203	13,593	13,450	15,106	15,738	16,733	21,023	22,153
Average Hourly Utilization	140	168	159	169	160	178	177	181	201	190

Source: FAA Statistical Handbook for years shown.

Figure 37

ESTIMATED AVERAGE ANNUAL UTILIZATION BY AIRCRAFT TYPE — HISTORICAL DATA 1953-1967

Aircraft Type	Average Annual Hours Flown per Aircraft									
	1953	1957	1960	1961	1962	1963	1964	1965	1966	1967
Single Engine 1-3 Place Recip.	132	124	121	119	123	131	137	147	164	185
Single Engine 4+ Place Recip.	169	199	165	161	162	182	176	177	195	179
Multi Engine	328	317	291	276	271	288	280	273	304	257
Multi-Engine Turbine	—	—	—	375	441	445	437	454	483	428
Rotorcraft	325	362	329	308	265	330	342	317	303	283
Other	39	72	51	63	77	91	88	90	78	59
Average Hourly Utilization	140	168	169	169	160	178	177	181	201	194

Source: FAA Statistical Handbook for years shown.

The SPEAS forecast of annual hours flown, projects a 7.6 percent annual compound growth rate through the forecast period going from 24.3 million hours in 1967 to 63.4 million in 1980. The largest growth rate increase per year is expected to occur in the multi-engine under 12,500 lb. turboprop classification, where hours

flown are estimated to grow 22 percent annually. This growth is primarily accounted for by the large air taxi use expected in the under 12,500 lb. turboprop category. Large annual increases are also expected in the over 12,500 lb. turboprop and turbojet fleets. The turbine powered fleets, because of their high initial cost and high performance capabilities, tend to result in higher utilization and subsequently the production of more total flight hours than smaller and less advanced equipment.

The largest percentage of total hours flown will continue to be accounted for by the reciprocating fleet, which today accounts for about 94 percent of total hours flown. This rate is projected to gradually taper off to a point where the piston engine type equipment should account for approximately 85 percent of all General Aviation hours flown in 1980. Figure 38 shows the annual hours flown by type of aircraft.

Utilization per aircraft is expected to go from 200 hours per year in 1967 to 244 hours in 1980 — a 1.6 percent compound growth rate. The turbine fleet will continue to experience a high utilization per aircraft as explained.

Figure 39 shows the projected average annual hourly utilization by type of aircraft in the active fleet. Figure 40 is a graph showing the history and projection of aircraft annual utilization in terms of hours per year. Figure 41 shows a plot of annual utilization by aircraft type as of 1967/68.

Average utilization rates by state and by SMSAs and estimated resultant flying hours are presented in Figures 42 and 43 respectively. In these figures, no values are shown where the resulting total hours were 500 or less. The totals in these figures will seldom add due to these and other rounding decisions. The values presented are considered reasonably to represent the actuals, but it must be acknowledged that this area of the analysis represents the greatest requirement for judgmental evaluation.

(Figures 38, 38a, 39, 40, 41, 42 and 43 follow)

Figure 38

FORECAST OF ANNUAL HOURS FLOWN IN GENERAL AVIATION
BY TYPE OF AIRCRAFT
1967-1980

Type of Aircraft	1967*	Annual Hours (in '000) Flown By The Active Fleet		
		1968	1975	1980
Single Engine 1-3 Place Reciprocating	8,573	9,117	12,742	14,088
Single Engine 4+ Place Reciprocating	10,579	11,056	18,658	30,219
Multi-Engine to 12,500 lbs. Under 600 H.P. Reciprocating	2,394	2,608	4,777	6,500
Multi-Engine to 12,500 lbs. Over 600 H.P. Reciprocating	870	939	2,046	3,132
Multi-Engine Over 12,500 lbs. Reciprocating	398	399	248	125
Multi-Engine Under 12,500 lbs. Turboprop	207	338	1,320	2,880
Multi-Engine Over 12,500 lbs. Turboprop	189	197	625	1,197
Multi-Engine Turbojet	324	426	1,131	2,205
Rotorcraft — All	681	779	1,466	3,045
Unspecified	128	153	165	190
Total Hours — All Types	24,343	26,012	43,178	63,581

*Reflects SPEAS adjustment of 1967 data published by FAA.

Sourse: SPEAS Analysis.

Figure 38a
ANNUAL HOURS FLOWN IN GENERAL AVIATION
BY TYPE OF AIRCRAFT
1967-1980

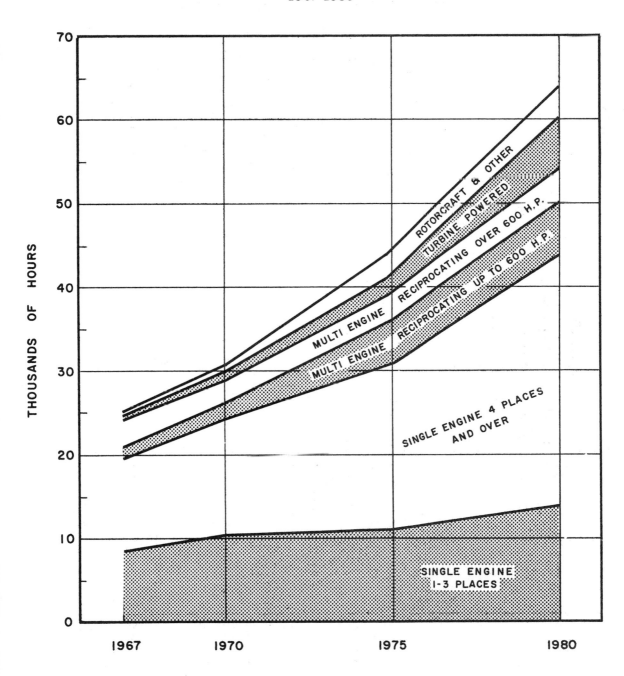

SOURCE: SPEAS ANALYSIS

Figure 39

GENERAL AVIATION AIRCRAFT
FORECAST AVERAGE HOURLY UTILIZATION BY TYPE
1967-1980

Type of Aircraft	Average Annual Hourly Utilization		
	1967/68*	1975	1980
Single Engine 1-3 Place Reciprocating	206	230	240
Single Engine 4+ Place Reciprocating	172	190	210
Multi-Engine to 12,500 lbs. Up To 600 H.P. Reciprocating	230	245	250
Multi-Engine to 12,500 lbs. Over 600 H.P. Reciprocating	307	330	360
Multi-Engine Over 12,500 lbs. Reciprocating	328/338	310	250
Multi-Engine Under 12,500 lbs. Turboprop	439/483	550	600
Multi-Engine Over 12,500 lbs. Turboprop	608/618	625	630
Multi-Engine Turbojet	414/452	435	450
Rotorcraft — All	365	349	350
Unspecified	113	97	100
Average Utilization — All Types	200	223	244

*Reflects SPEAS adjustment of 1967 data published by the FAA. Utilization rates are the same for both 1967 and 1968 for all categories except those showing two values, which are indicated for 1967/68.

Source: SPEAS Analysis.

Figure 40
GENERAL AVIATION
AVERAGE ANNUAL HOURS OF UTILIZATION
FOR 1967 AND 1968

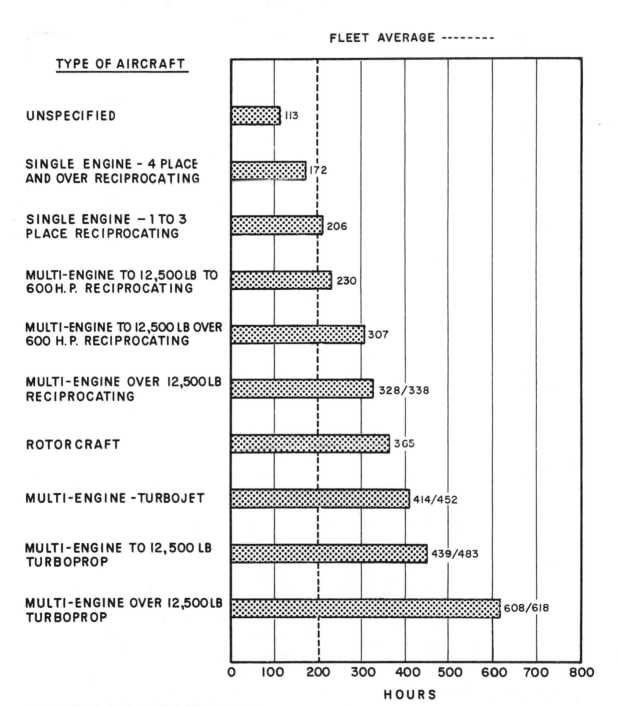

NOTE: WHERE TWO VALUES ARE SHOWN,
REFERENCE IS MADE TO 1967 AND 1968

SOURCE: SPEAS ANALYSIS

Figure 41

GENERAL AVIATION
AVERAGE ANNUAL HOURS OF UTILIZATION
BY TYPE OF AIRCRAFT
1953-1980

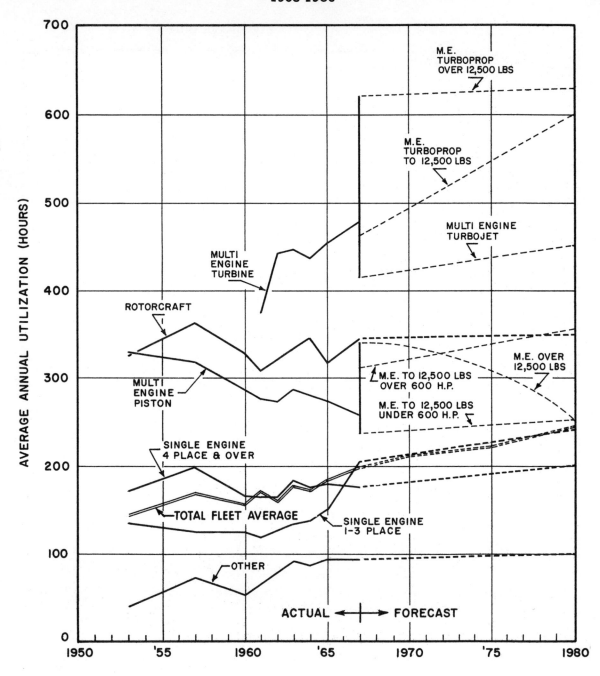

SOURCE: SPEAS ANALYSIS

Figure 42

AIRCRAFT UTILIZATION AND FLIGHT HOURS
DETAIL BY CATEGORY BY STATES
(Flight Hours in Thousands)

		SE 1-3	SE 4+	ME 600—	ME 600+	ME 12.5+	ME 12.5—T	ME 12.5+T	T/J	Rotor	Other	Total
Alabama	Utilization	170	170	255	285	325	460/485	620/635	415/435	340/325	95/100	
	1967 Hours	100	129	46	7	6	3	1	3	2	1	298
	1968 Hours	138	108	38	7	6	2	1	3	2	1	306
Arizona	Utilization	230	180	205	300	325			415/435	340/325	95/100	
	1967 Hours	146	177	29	13	10			2	13	2	393
	1968 Hours	147	197	32	11	8			1	20	2	418
Arkansas	Utilization	230	165	235	210	325	460/485		415/435	340/325	95/100	
	1967 Hours	153	122	39	10	3	2		2	2		330
	1968 Hours	164	128	42	10	3	4		3	2		354
California	Utilization	240	160	205	275	325	460/485	620/635	415/435	340/325	95/100	
	1967 Hours	1,424	1,480	248	78	53	18	8	35	114	26	3,480
	1968 Hours	1,519	1,528	260	76	53	38	8	50	125	32	3,673
Colorado	Utilization	240	180	225	235	325	460/485	620/635	415/435	340/325	95/100	
	1967 Hours	157	194	39	8	2	3	2	4	6	3	419
	1968 Hours	165	209	41	10	3	4	3	9	11	3	458
Connecticut	Utilization	200	170	230	325	325	460/485	620/635	415/435	340/325	95/100	
	1967 Hours	73	89	20	4	1	3		3	8	2	204
	1968 Hours	78	93	24	4	1	5		2	7	2	216
Delaware	Utilization	180	150	235	325	325	460/485	620/635	415/435	340/325	95/100	
	1967 Hours	23	34	14	9	1	3	2	10	1	1	99
	1968 Hours	25	36	18	10	1	8	4	13	2		118
District of Columbia	Utilization	215	360	285	755	760	460/485	620/635	415/435	340/325	95/100	
	1967 Hours	11	136	14	42	59	2	12	5	8	3	291
	1968 Hours	11	135	15	43	71	4	15	6	7	3	310
Florida	Utilization	280	185	225	240	325	460/485	620/635	415/435	340/325	95/100	
	1967 Hours	510	442	122	38	35	6	2	9	26	3	1,191
	1968 Hours	525	463	129	38	38	12	2	5	35	4	1,250
Georgia	Utilization	235	170	230	310	325	460/485	620/635	415/435	340/325	95/100	
	1967 Hours	204	187	59	19	4	3	4	10	5	10	505
	1968 Hours	225	208	67	20	3	7	2	15	5	10	560

(Continued on Next Page)

Figure 42

(Continued from Preceding Page)

State		SE 1-3	SE 4+	ME 600-	ME 600+	ME 12.5+	ME 12.5-T	ME 12.5+T	T/J	Rotor	Other	Total
Idaho	Utilization	170	155	210	270	325			415/435	340/325	95/100	
	1967 Hours	64	96	10	4	1			1	10	1	187
	1968 Hours	68	96	12	4	1			2	10	1	194
Illinois	Utilization	190	165	210	310	325	460/485	620/635	415/435	340/325	95/100	
	1967 Hours	329	529	114	42	13	8	9	25	17	4	1,085
	1968 Hours	350	546	113	42	9	18	6	37	20	4	1,140
Indiana	Utilization	165	150	235	350	325	460/485	620/635	415/435	340/325	95/100	
	1967 Hours	149	267	78	32	8	5	4	4	10	2	559
	1968 Hours	162	267	84	35	10	8	4	5	10	2	587
Iowa	Utilization	165	160	285	415	325	460/485		415/435	340/325	95/100	
	1967 Hours	125	250	63	17	1	2		1	4	1	460
	1968 Hours	131	255	61	24		3			6	1	480
Kansas	Utilization	205	175	255	215	325	460/485		415/435	340/325	95/100	
	1967 Hours	188	297	59	11	3	5		5	6	2	575
	1968 Hours	191	318	61	12	3	6		6	7	2	605
Kentucky	Utilization	205	175	305	310	325	460/485		415/435	340/325		
	1967 Hours	59	77	29	9	2	2		2	4		182
	1968 Hours	68	82	38	10	3	2		3	3		209
Louisiana	Utilization	260	215	250	290		460/485	620/635	415/435	800/790		
	1967 Hours	210	169	46	15		1	3	2	123		569
	1968 Hours	218	183	49	17		2	2	2	134		607
Maine	Utilization	120	150	275						340/325		
	1967 Hours	33	32	11						2		78
	1968 Hours	35	35	13						3		86
Maryland	Utilization	185	150	235	310	325	460/485	620/635	415/435	340/325	95/100	
	1967 Hours	94	95	21	9	4	3	10	5	15	3	259
	1968 Hours	99	111	28	12	3	4	6	4	11	2	280
Massachusetts	Utilization	200	160	230	380	325	460/485	620/635	415/435	340/325	95/100	
	1967 Hours	117	121	34	11	2	5	1	7	10	3	311
	1968 Hours	136	131	36	13	2	6	3	10	9	4	350
Michigan	Utilization	150	145	315	310	325	460/485	620/635	415/435	340/325	95/100	
	1967 Hours	250	415	94	44	5	12	22	5	11	3	865
	1968 Hours	265	429	100	48	8	16	22	8	11	4	910
Minnesota	Utilization	150	175	220	230	325	460/485	620/635	415/435	340/325	95/100	
	1967 Hours	202	298	37	10	4	4	8	8	11	1	581
	1968 Hours	214	311	40	12	4	5	6	14	11	2	616

(Continued on Next Page)

Figure 42

(Continued from Preceding Page)

State		SE 1-3	SE 4+	ME 600-	ME 600+	ME 12.5+	ME 12.5-T	ME 12.5+T	T/J	Rotor	Other	Total
Mississippi	Utilization	230	170	225	250	325	460/485		415/435	340/325	95/100	
	1967 Hours	146	100	26	8	3				3	1	287
	1968 Hours	151	103	28	8	1	4		2	3	1	301
Missouri	Utilization	180	165	235	335	280	460/485	620/635	415/435	340/325	95/100	
	1967 Hours	177	283	65	26	8	3		13	9	2	586
	1968 Hours	194	299	68	35	3	8	1	15	9	2	631
Montana	Utilization	135	165	210	260	325	460/485			340/325		
	1967 Hours	76	128	18	4	2	2			6		236
	1968 Hours	78	132	17	5	2	1			8		243
Nebraska	Utilization	160	165	220	295	325		620/635	415/435	340/325	95/100	
	1967 Hours	105	136	28	8	3		1	5	7		293
	1968 Hours	111	141	33	9	3			5	8	1	311
Nevada	Utilization	280	180	270	235	325	460/485	620/635	415/435	340/325	95/100	
	1967 Hours	81	86	22	4	4	3	1	2	11	1	215
	1968 Hours	76	97	25	5	7	2		3	4	2	221
New Hampshire	Utilization	165	160	260	310	325		620/635	415/435	340/325	95/100	
	1967 Hours	22	30	7	2							61
	1968 Hours	23	30	8	1			1	1	1		65
New Jersey	Utilization	200	140	220	240	325	460/485	620/635	415/435	340/325	95/100	
	1967 Hours	176	193	55	11	4	1	7	6	12	3	468
	1968 Hours	192	197	59	9	4	9	8	10	14	3	505
New Mexico	Utilization	210	190	235	285	325		620/635	415/435	340/325	95/100	
	1967 Hours	61	150	27	3	2		1	2	2	1	247
	1968 Hours	58	155	31	6	2		1	5	5	2	260
New York	Utilization	185	150	220	300	325	460/485	620/635	415/435	340/325	95/100	
	1967 Hours	340	361	89	38	25	23	38	70	25	9	1,015
	1968 Hours	360	381	100	40	17	44	42	80	31	10	1,100
North Carolina	Utilization	185	160	245	320	325	460/485	620/635	415/435	340/325	95/100	
	1967 Hours	132	176	53	15	3	5	2	2	8	1	397
	1968 Hours	135	180	61	19	3	9	6	5	7	2	427
North Dakota	Utilization	145	175	260	215							
	1967 Hours	84	68	8								160
	1968 Hours	86	69	10		2						167
Ohio	Utilization	160	145	245	300	325	460/485	620/635	415/435	340/325	95/100	
	1967 Hours	288	421	119	47	15	17	16	22	20	6	978
	1968 Hours	300	430	136	51	14	26	17	28	20	6	1,030

(Continued on Next Page)

80

Figure 42
(Continued from Preceding Page)

	SE 1-3	SE 4+	ME 600—	ME 600+	ME 12.5+	ME 12.5—T	ME 12.5+T	T/J	Rotor	Other	Total
Oklahoma Utilization	235	180	265	310	325	460/485	620/635	415/435	340/325	95/100	
1967 Hours	197	230	53	26	6	12	4	7	17	1	553
1968 Hours	240	249	70	27	7	12	3	11	16	1	636
Oregon Utilization	165	150	190	275	325	460/485	620/635	415/435	340/325	95/100	
1967 Hours	133	216	39	18	6	1	1	1	23	1	439
1968 Hours	138	219	35	18	4	1	1	2	34	6	454
Pennsylvania Utilization	150	135	240	360	325	460/485	620/635	415/435	340/325	95/100	
1967 Hours	195	282	95	34	12	11	12	14	21	5	683
1968 Hours	200	300	102	37	14	19	13	21	26	6	740
Rhode Island Utilization	195	175	285	280		460/485			340/325		
1967 Hours	12	16	4	1		1			2	1	35
1968 Hours	13	20	4	1					3	1	43
South Carolina Utilization	195	170	265	290	325	460/485		415/435	340/325	95/100	
1967 Hours	65	78	30	10	2	2		1	6	1	195
1968 Hours	73	80	33	9	3	3		2	10	2	215
South Dakota Utilization	145	155	210	365	325				340/325		
1967 Hours	66	66	8	3	1				1		145
1968 Hours	60	66	7	3	1				1		138
Tennessee Utilization	195	175	240	360	325	460/485	620/635	415/435	340/325	95/100	
1967 Hours	95	145	60	23	6	5	15	5	4	1	344
1968 Hours	99	151	59	21	6	7	12	5	4	2	355
Texas Utilization	225	175	225	280	300	460/485	620/635	415/435	340/325	95/100	
1967 Hours	770	861	202	86	56	18	15	15	39	8	2,066
1968 Hours	801	878	232	90	53	26	12	22	48	10	2,170
Utah Utilization	190	175	195	305	325				340/325	95/100	
1967 Hours	41	76	10	4	2				4	1	137
1968 Hours	37	82	13	5	2				6		144
Vermont Utilization	160	145	225	355	325	460/485		415/435		95/100	
1967 Hours	15	15	8	2	1	1		1		2	44
1968 Hours	16	17	7	6	1	1				2	51
Virginia Utilization	195	155	215	400	325	460/485	620/635	415/435	340/325	95/100	
1967 Hours	109	121	28	14	1	2	2	2	3	2	284
1968 Hours	121	130	32	17	1	2	2	2	6	3	315
Washington Utilization	200	165	215	330	325	460/485	620/635	415/435	340/325	95/100	
1967 Hours	214	248	27	8	2	2	1	5	19	3	529
1968 Hours	240	281	36	8	2	3		3	24	4	601

(Continued on Next Page)

The Magnitude and Economic Impact of General Aviation — 1968-1980

Figure 42

(Continued from Preceding Page)

		SE 1-3	SE 4+	ME 600—	ME 600+	ME 12.5+	ME 12.5—T	ME 12.5+T	T/J	Rotor	Other	Total
West Virginia	Utilization	140	155	250	300		460/485			340/325	95/100	
	1967 Hours	20	42	13	6					2		83
	1968 Hours	22	48	18	6		1			2	1	98
Wisconsin	Utilization	150	155	230	375	325	460/485	620/635	415/435	340/325	95/100	
	1967 Hours	137	171	44	28	6	3	1	3	4	1	398
	1968 Hours	145	178	50	24	7	7	2	6	6	1	426
Wyoming	Utilization	160	170	185	175	325		620/635		340/325		
	1967 Hours	34	56	6	2	7		1		3		109
	1968 Hours	34	57	5	3	7		1		3		109
Alaska	Utilization	150	205	245	230	325	460/485		415/435	340/325		
	1967 Hours	127	170	10	4	3	2			17		333
	1968 Hours	141	201	13	5	3	4		1	25		393
Hawaii	Utilization	460	225	440	650	325	460/485		415/435	340/325	95/100	
	1967 Hours	29	12	11	5	2	1		1	2	1	64
	1968 Hours	35	13	10	7	1			1	4	1	71
Total	1967 Hours	8,573	10,579	2,394	870	398	207	189	324	681	128	24,343
	1968 Hours	9,117	11,056	2,608	939	399	338	197	426	779	153	26,012

Note: Aircraft type abbreviations used are:

Reciprocating Engine

SE 1-3	Single Engine, 1-3 Place
SE 4+	Single Engine, 4 or more Places
ME 600—	Multi-Engine, to 12,500 lbs., to 600 HP
ME 600+	Multi-Engine, to 12,500 lbs., over 600 HP
ME 12.5+	Multi-Engine, over 12,500 lbs.

Turbine Engine

ME 12.5—T	Turboprop Single and Multi-Engine, to 12,500 lbs.
ME 12.5+T	Turboprop Single and Multi-Engine, over 12,500 lbs.
	Turbo-Jet
	Rotorcraft
	Unspecified or Other

Totals may not add due to rounding.

Source: SPEAS Analysis.

Figure 43

AIRCRAFT UTILIZATION AND FLIGHT HOURS
DETAIL BY CATEGORY BY SMSA
(Flight Hours in Thousands)

SMSA Area	Year	SE 1-3	SE 4+	ME 600-	ME 600+	ME 12.5+	ME 12.5-T	ME 12.5+T	T/J	Rotor	Other	Total
New York	Utilization	285	170	210	305	360	470/500	635/650	415/435	350	105/110	
	1967 Hours	175	159	48	20	24	14	29	61	14	2	547
	1968 Hours	186	173	55	23	12	34	34	73	20	3	612
Chicago	Utilization	200	170	200	335	360	470/500	635/650	415/435	350	105/110	
	1967 Hours	150	272	66	22	8	4	8	14	12	3	559
	1968 Hours	155	264	68	23	6	12	5	30	13	2	578
Los Angeles	Utilization	255	160	205	260	360	470/500	635/650	415/435	350	105/110	
	1967 Hours	345	378	73	30	34	8	4	18	56	9	955
	1968 Hours	373	376	79	33	30	18	4	35	61	12	1,021
Philadelphia	Utilization	180	145	210	370	360	470/500	635/650	415/435	350	105/110	
	1967 Hours	77	95	24	13	9	5	5	5	14	2	249
	1968 Hours	87	106	26	13	6	9	5	5	14	2	273
Detroit	Utilization	175	145	185	280	360	470/500	635/650	415/435	350	105/110	
	1967 Hours	74	143	35	19	5	6	7	2	6	2	299
	1968 Hours	79	146	38	19	4	7	13	4	5	2	318
Boston	Utilization	205	165	260	395	360	470/500	635/650	415/435	350	105/110	
	1967 Hours	61	66	20	6	2	3	1	7	6	3	176
	1968 Hours	73	69	22	8	1	6	3	9	6	2	199
San Francisco	Utilization	260	170	180	230	540	470/500	635/650	415/435	350	105/110	
	1967 Hours	179	173	31	12	12	2	1	5	7	4	428
	1968 Hours	171	186	28	9	6	5	3	9	11	7	434
Pittsburgh	Utilization	170	140	235	255	360	470/500	635/650	415/435	350	105/110	
	1867 Hours	42	48	14	3	4	4	5	7	4	1	131
	1968 Hours	43	55	16	5	4	7	7	11	4	1	153
St. Louis	Utilization	195	190	245	265	220	470/500	635/650	415/435	350	105/110	
	1967 Hours	64	98	29	10	3	1	4	7	4	2	221
	1968 Hours	64	99	22	18	2	4	1	12	3	1	227
Washington, D.C.	Utilization	215	280	250	735	730	470/500	635/650	415/435	350	105/110	
	1967 Hours	79	238	27	43	40	2	4	2	14	1	451
	1968 Hours	88	252	34	53	72	5	10	6	12	6	537

(Continued on Next Page)

Figure 43

(Continued from Preceding Page)

SMSA Area	Year	SE 1-3	SE 4+	ME 600—	ME 600+	ME 12.5+	ME 12.5—T	ME 12.5+T	T/J	Rotor	Other	Total
Cleveland	Utilization	170	135	245	395	360	470/500	635/650	415/435	350	105/110	
	1967 Hours	34	60	19	11	2	3	3	2	4	1	140
	1968 Hours	38	58	26	16	3	5	2	4	5	1	157
Baltimore	Utilization	165	155	195	310	360	470/500	635/650	415/435	350	105/110	
	1967 Hours	37	43	8	6	1	1	1	5	3	1	105
	1968 Hours	35	44	8	7	1	2	1	4	2	1	106
Newark	Utilization	185	150	225	365		470/500	635/650	415/435	350	105/110	
	1967 Hours	35	48	14	2			1	2	2	1	107
	1968 Hours	33	50	16	2		3	1	4	5	1	116
Minneapolis	Utilization	200	190	225	270	360	470/500	635/650	415/435	350	105/110	
	1967 Hours	102	136	24	8	4	2	5	11	6	1	300
	1968 Hours	106	142	26	9	4	4	7	13	7	1	317
Houston	Utilization	195	180	240	275	360	470/500	635/650	415/435	350	105/110	
	1967 Hours	94	122	34	20	19	4	9	5	7	2	316
	1968 Hours	80	124	40	15	19	8	7	7	11	1	311
Buffalo	Utilization	150	140	200	310	360	470/500	635/650	415/435	350		
	1967 Hours	17	20	4	1	2		1	1	2		47
	1968 Hours	21	19	6	2	3		1		3		55
Milwaukee	Utilization	170	170	230	275	360	470/500	635/650	415/435	350	105/110	
	1967 Hours	37	54	15	6	3	1	1	1	3	1	122
	1968 Hours	38	60	17	6	3	2	2	1	3	1	133
Cincinnati	Utilization	180	165	220	210	360	470/500	635/650	415/435	350	105/110	
	1967 Hours	21	35	12	4	2	2	3	1	2	1	80
	1968 Hours	24	33	12	4	2	1	3	4	2	1	85
Paterson	Utilization	240	160	225	155	360	470/500	635/650	415/435	350	105/110	
	1967 Hours	33	49	16	2	1	1	1	2	1	1	104
	1968 Hours	37	49	20	3		2	2	3	1	1	118
Dallas	Utilization	225	165	230	385	300	470/500	635/650	415/435	350	105/110	
	1967 Hours	89	112	40	20	15	2	1	5	2	2	289
	1968 Hours	91	120	45	22	11	4	2	7	3	3	308
Seattle	Utilization	245	170	220	195	360	470/500	635/650	415/435	350	105/110	
	1967 Hours	104	97	13	2	1	1	1	5	6	3	232
	1968 Hours	113	119	18	2				3	11	3	271
Kansas City	Utilization	230	155	230	375	360	470/500	635/650	415/435	350	105/110	
	1967 Hours	77	89	26	8	6	2	1	5	4	1	216
	1968 Hours	88	96	32	9		2		2	6	1	235

(Continued on Next Page)

Figure 43

(Continued from Preceding Page)

SMSA Area	Year	SE 1-3	SE 4+	ME 600—	ME 600+	ME 12.5+	ME 12.5—T	ME 12.5+T	T/J	Rotor	Other	Total
San Diego	Utilization	280	185	290	465	360	470/500	635/650	415/435	350	105/110	
	1967 Hours	86	97	26	8	2		1	1	4	3	227
	1968 Hours	83	107	33	6	1		1	4	7	3	245
Atlanta	Utilization	245	165	225	300	360	470/500	635/650	415/435	350	105/110	
	1967 Hours	84	89	28	11	4	1	4	5	3	1	229
	1968 Hours	87	96	29	11	3	2	2	10	3	1	243
Indianapolis	Utilization	135	135	230	340	360	470/500	635/650	415/435	350	105/110	
	1967 Hours	28	61	21	10	2	2	4	1	2	1	130
	1968 Hours	29	59	23	9	4	1	2	1	2	1	130
Miami	Utilization	360	215	240	240	360	470/500	635/650	415/435	350	105/110	
	1967 Hours	149	74	25	12	21	1	3	5	5	1	295
	1968 Hours	152	76	30	12	17		3	3	8	1	301
Denver	Utilization	290	190	235	245	360	470/500	635/650	415/435	350	105/110	
	1967 Hours	89	102	26	7	2	3	3	3	4	1	239
	1968 Hours	95	103	28	8	3	4	4	8	10	1	264
New Orleans	Utilization	255	265	220	300	360	470/500	635/650	415/435	850/830		
	1967 Hours	24	39	10	3	1		1	1	83		163
	1968 Hours	23	39	10	3	4	1	1	1	83		165
Portland	Utilization	185	160	200	285	360	470/500	635/650	415/435	350	105/110	
	1967 Hours	60	97	24	14	1	1	1	1	8		207
	1968 Hours	64	96	20	12	1	1	1	1	14	1	211
San Bernadino	Utilization	220	170	170	340	360	470/500			350	105/110	
	1967 Hours	82	90	12	4	1				7	2	198
	1968 Hours	84	96	11	5	1	1			7	3	208
Tampa	Utilization	290	190	250	440	360			415/435	350		
	1967 Hours	37	45	15	5	3			1	3		109
	1968 Hours	37	46	14	3	3				4		107
Columbus	Utilization	225	185	260	270	360	470/500	635/650	415/435	350	105/110	
	1967 Hours	32	49	15	5	5	1	1	2	4	1	115
	1968 Hours	31	52	18	5	3	4	1	7	3	1	125
Rochester	Utilization	115	160	210	300	360	470/500	635/650		350	105/110	
	1967 Hours	13	29	47	3	1	1	1			1	53
	1968 Hours	14	31	5	3	1	1	2			1	58
Dayton	Utilization	170	160	215	330	360	470/500	635/650	415/435	350	105/110	
	1967 Hours	28	39	9	3	1	1	1		3	1	84
	1968 Hours	32	49	1	4	1	1	2	1	2	1	104

(Continued on Next Page)

Figure 43

(Continued from Preceding Page)

SMSA Area	Year	SE 1-3	SE 4+	ME 600—	ME 600+	ME 12.5+	ME 12.5—T	ME 12.5+T	T/J	Rotor	Other	Total
Louisville	Utilization	240	185	350	265	360	470/500	635/650		350		
	1967 Hours	20	21	14	1	1		1		1		59
	1968 Hours	19	23	16	2			1		1		62
Birmingham	Utilization	195	185	225	285	360	470/500	635/650	415/435			
	1967 Hours	10	26	12	3		2	1				54
	1968 Hours	8	26	12	3	1	2	1	1			52
Providence	Utilization	200	160	185	265					350		
	1967 Hours	9	10	1	1					4		25
	1968 Hours	10	13	1	1					4		29
San Antonio	Utilization	235	170	200	200	360	470/500	635/650		350	105/110	
	1967 Hours	25	37	18	6	4	2	1		3	1	97
	1968 Hours	29	32	18	7	3	1	1		3	1	95
Anaheim	Utilization	255	155	145	200	360	470/500	635/650		350	105/110	
	1967 Hours	73	86	11	2	3	1			5	4	185
	1968 Hours	88	96	13	2	3		1		8	4	215
Hartford	Utilization	185	195	290	365	360	470/500		415/435	350		
	1967 Hours	17	27	9	2		2		2	3		62
	1968 Hours	18	30	9	3	1	2		1	1		65
Memphis	Utilization	240	175	205	285	360	470/500	635/650	415/435	350		
	1967 Hours	39	49	17	7	2	3		2	2		121
	1968 Hours	39	49	16	8	3	4	1	3	2		125
Phoenix	Utilization	245	180	185	330	360	470/500		415/435	350	105/110	
	1967 Hours	87	88	13	8	7			2	12	1	218
	1968 Hours	94	99	17	9	8	1		1	15	2	246
New Haven	Utilization	225	195	235	380	360			415/435	350		
	1967 Hours	12	15	3	2					4		36
	1968 Hours	14	16	5	1					3		40
Albany	Utilization	120	135	225	275	360	470/500	635/650		350	105/110	
	1967 Hours	10	15	4	2	1					1	33
	1968 Hours	14	16	3	1			1	1			37
Stamford	Utilization	240	155	160	235		470/500		415/435	350	105/110	
	1967 Hours	19	24	4	1				1	1	1	51
	1968 Hours	23	28	6	1					3	1	63
San Jose	Utilization	275	185	190	230		470/500			350	105/110	
	1967 Hours	99	111	15	3					2	2	232
	1968 Hours	100	116	17	4		2			2	2	243

(Continued on Next Page)

Figure 43

(Continued from Preceding Page)

SMSA Area	Year	SE 1-3	SE 4+	ME 600—	ME 600+	ME 12.5+	ME 12.5—T	ME 12.5+T	T/J	Rotor	Other	Total
Toledo	Utilization	150	145	425	280	360	470/500	635/650	415/435	350	105/110	
	1967 Hours	12	27	17	4	1	1	3	3	1		69
	1968 Hours	13	28	14	4	1	2	4	3		1	70
Sacramento	Utilization	240	165	220	180	360				350	105/110	
	1967 Hours	72	62	10	1	1				1	1	147
	1968 Hours	71	72	7						2	1	153
Jersey City	Utilization	95	120	175				635/650	415/435			
	1967 Hours	1	2	2				1	1			7
	1968 Hours	1	2	2				2	1			7
Akron	Utilization	160	135	255	265	360	470/500	635/650	415/435	350	105/110	
	1967 Hours	13	23	6	3	4		1	2	1	1	54
	1968 Hours	15	25	7	4	3		2	4	2	1	65
Worcester	Utilization	135	135	125	270	360	470/500	635/650	415/435	350	105/110	
	1967 Hours	11	14	2	1			1		1		29
	1968 Hours	12	15	2	1		2		1	2	1	35
Norfolk	Utilization	250	155	175	365		470/500	635/650		350		
	1967 Hours	9	8	1				1		2		20
	1968 Hours	11	8	2						1		24
Gary	Utilization	190	140	150	275		470/500					
	1967 Hours	10	18	2	1		1					30
	1968 Hours	13	21	4								40
Fort Worth	Utilization	240	160	280	275	360	470/500	635/650	415/435	350	105/110	
	1967 Hours	63	60	15	5	4	1	3		13	1	165
	1968 Hours	76	66	20	6	4	1	1	1	17	1	193
Syracuse	Utilization	125	135	200	355	360	470/500			350		
	1967 Hours	11	19	6	5	1				2		44
	1968 Hours	13	19	4	5		1			1		43
Springfield	Utilization	220	150	240								
	1967 Hours	13	15	3								31
	1968 Hours	16	17	4								37
Greensboro	Utilization	140	170	250	270		470/500	635/650	415/435	350		
	1967 Hours	17	36	11	3		3	3	1			74
	1968 Hours	16	39	11	3		4	5	3			82
Oklahoma City	Utilization	205	180	240	280	360	470/500		415/435	350	105/110	
	1967 Hours	32	62	20	10	4	9		5	2		144
	1968 Hours	37	68	24	9	4	9		6	1	1	158

(Continued on Next Page)

Figure 43

(Continued from Preceding Page)

SMSA Area	Year	SE 1-3	SE 4+	ME 600-	ME 600+	ME 12.5+	ME 12.5-T	ME 12.5+T	T/J	Rotor	Other	Total
Youngstown	Utilization	150	155	230	320		470/500	635/650	415/435	350		
	1967 Hours	13	14	5	6		4	1	3	1		47
	1968 Hours	12	16	7	3		6	1	3	1		49
Honolulu	Utilization	450	225	430	650	360					105/110	
	1967 Hours	28	10	8	6	1				2	1	56
	1968 Hours	30	10	9	7	1				2	1	60
Allentown	Utilization	145	115	215	440	360		635/650	415/435			
	1967 Hours	9	10	2	2			1	2			26
	1968 Hours	10	11	3	1	1		1	3			30
Nashville	Utilization	180	190	270	360	360	470/500		415/435	350	105/110	
	1967 Hours	9	19	11	6	4	2		3	1	1	56
	1968 Hours	10	18	10	3	1	4		2	1	1	50
Grand Rapids	Utilization	140	150	225	350		470/500				105/110	
	1967 Hours	15	30	5	3						1	54
	1968 Hours	15	30	6	4		1					56
Omaha	Utilization	210	170	240	320	360	470/500		415/435	350		
	1967 Hours	24	38	11	3	1			3			80
	1968 Hours	24	44	13	6	1	1		4	2		95
Jacksonville	Utilization	195	180	220	260	360	470/500	635/650	415/435	350		
	1967 Hours	10	17	8	2	1	1					39
	1968 Hours	12	18	6	2	1	2	1		1		43
Salt Lake City	Utilization	190	175	185	360	360				350	105/110	
	1967 Hours	18	35	5	3	1				2	1	65
	1968 Hours	14	36	8	4					2	1	65
Richmond	Utilization	165	175	235	310		470/500					
	1967 Hours	11	16	6	2							35
	1968 Hours	7	15	6	3		2					33
Tulsa	Utilization	330	170	330	385	360	470/500	635/650	415/435	350	105/110	
	1967 Hours	52	47	17	12	3	1		2	5	1	140
	1968 Hours	66	46	21	12	3	3	1	3	5		160
Flint	Utilization	115	130	215	280							
	1967 Hours	14	24	4	2							44
	1968 Hours	13	25	4	2							44
Wilmington	Utilization	145	150	215	365	360	470/500	635/650	415/435	350	105/110	
	1967 Hours	12	26	10	9	1	2	3	10			73
	1968 Hours	13	27	13	10	1	7	5	11	1	1	89

(Continued on Next Page)

Figure 43

(Continued from Preceding Page)

SMSA Area	Year	SE 1-3	SE 4+	ME 600—	ME 600+	ME 12.5+	ME 12.5—T	ME 12.5+T	T/J	Rotor	Other	Total
Wichita	Utilization	205	210	270	255	360	470/500		415/435	350	105/110	
	1967 Hours	48	97	28	9	2	3		4	1	1	193
	1968 Hours	41	110	24	9	2	6		4	3	2	201
Harrisburg	Utilization	170	135	270	340					350	105/110	
	1967 Hours	10	12	8	3					1	1	35
	1968 Hours	11	12	7	3					1	1	35
Knoxville	Utilization	200	140	260	350	360				350		
	1967 Hours	11	15	11	2							39
	1968 Hours	10	13	9	2	1				1		36
Fresno	Utilization	230	165	205	195		470/500			350		
	1967 Hours	37	41	10	2					4		94
	1968 Hours	40	42	10	1		1			4		98
Mobile	Utilization	220	175	290	360	360	470/500	635/650				
	1967 Hours	13	9	7	2	1	1	1				34
	1968 Hours	13	11	8	2	2	1	1				38
Total	1967 Hours	3,656	4,661	1,179	496	284	108	133	238	381	71	11,211
	1968 Hours	3,845	4,897	1,283	530	287	227	158	330	444	88	12,089

Note: Aircraft type abbreviations used are:

Reciprocating Engine

SE 1-3	Single Engine, 1-3 Place
SE 4+	Single Engine, 4 or more Places
ME 600—	Multi-Engine, to 12,500 lbs., to 600 HP
ME 600+	Multi-Engine, to 12,500 lbs., over 600 HP
ME 12.5+	Multi-Engine, over 12,500 lbs.

Turbine Engine

ME 12.5—T	Turboprop Single and Multi-Engine, to 12,500 lbs.
ME 12.5+T	Turboprop Single and Multi-Engine, over 12,500 lbs.
T/J	Turbo-Jet
Rotor	Rotorcraft
Other	Unspecified or Other

Totals may not add due to rounding.

Source: SPEAS Analysis.

CHAPTER FIVE

AIRCRAFT MOVEMENTS

To establish a base starting point for the determination of General Aviation movements, the past history of General Aviation activity was examined to ascertain what information was available. It was established from this review that the only published data was that registered at airports with FAA control towers, which amounted to only 313 airports in 1967, out of the national total of 10,126. It was judged that this information was not of sufficient depth to be representative of General Aviation activities.

A sampling technique was therefore considered which would generate meaningful data on aircraft movements in the United States. To obtain a representative nationwide sample, a study was made of the FAA tape and registration data on the General Aviation fleet by state distribution. From this development a percentile distribution for the 50 states and the District of Columbia was established. For example, the State of California accounted for nearly 14 percent of the General Aviation active aircraft fleet at the end of 1967, Michigan 4 percent, Iowa 2 percent and so on throughout the states. The sample from each state was then weighted in proportion to the total number of aircraft registered in the state.

The sample included 218 airports with varying degrees of General Aviation activity, with each state contributing sample airports in proportion to the active aircraft registered there.

A search was made for data that would concur with the foregoing sample analysis on movements. This review disclosed that three states, Michigan, Minnesota and Montana had completed similar research. The results of these findings appear in the following table:

State	Total Annual G. A. Movements	Total Based G. A. Aircraft	Annual Movements per Based Aircraft
Montana[1]	786,190	1,285	612
SPEAS 50 State Sample	23,900,533	29,810	802
Minnesota[2]	817,854	944	866
Michigan[3]	3,679,460	3,415	1,077

With the sample number of airports for each state established, an analysis and summary was made of local and itinerant movements plus based aircraft, as recorded on the most recent FAA field inspections shown on the Form 29As.

The SPEAS sample included the 144 large, medium and small hub cities — not only the large fields, but also the smaller General Aviation fields that help comprise the hub city.

The Form 29As record a count of based aircraft and an estimate of the local and itinerant General Aviation operations plus an actual count of these operations at those fields with FAA tower facilities.

The sample included 29,810 based General Aviation aircraft, which is 26 percent of the 114,400 aircraft the FAA has indicated were in the inventory at December 31, 1967.

Since an acceptable correlation does exist between based aircraft and movements, this methodology was applied to the sampling technique. The average number of 1967 movements per General Aviation aircraft was then calculated to be 802. This figure varies, of course, between types of aircraft, with rotorcraft and single engine 1-3 place types accounting for the bulk of the movements. Because of the lack of reliable industry trend data of an historical nature on movements, forecasts of these values through 1980 required making several analytical judgments to project a growth

Source: [1]Montana Airport Status Sheet
[2]Aviation Survey—Twin City Metropolitan Area
[3]Michigan Aviation Fact Finder

rate through the forecast period. It was estimated that the growth would occur at approximately a 1 percent compound rate, which would
increase the movements from 802 in 1967 to
929 in 1980.

By applying the annual movements per aircraft to the fleet population, (see Figure 44)
it was calculated that there were 98 million
General Aviation total movements in the United
States in 1967. The "FAA Air Traffic Activity"
publication for calendar year 1967 indicated that
there were 37.2 million General Aviation local
and itinerant operations at those fields having
control towers; this accounts for approximately 38 percent of all General Aviation
movements. The SPEAS forecast indicates that
local and itinerant movements in the U. S. will
more than double by 1980, rising from 98 million in 1967 to over 237 million in 1980. Figure
45 shows the fleet breakdown by total annual
movements.

The analysis of the Form 29As also indicated the division between local and itinerant
movements, but not between IFR and VFR.
In this study of 1967 operations, itinerant
movements accounted for 52.8 percent of the
total. This value confirmed data published by
the FAA with respect to tower airport operations, which showed the following history of
itinerant operations as a percent of total recorded:

1956	53.6%	1962	59.7%
1957	54.5%	1963	58.5%
1958	56.5%	1964	56.4%
1959	57.5%	1965	55.4%
1960	60.0%	1966	53.8%
1961	60.7%	1967	52.8%

(29A Data)

This swing in operations can be rationalized
by the major drop of instructional flying which
occurred in the early 1960s, and the recovery
from this lull has brought local operations back
to the relative level which they achieved in the
1950s. It is forecast that, with the growth in
students projected to increase but at a reduced
rate, the proportion of itinerant movements will
drop slightly to 50 percent of total movements

in 1980. The indicated split of operations in the
forecast period is as follows (in thousands of
movements):

Year	Local	Itinerant	Total
1967	46,300	51,700	98,000
1975	83,700	85,000	168,700
1980	118,700	118,700	237,400

General Aviation IFR operations have experienced a compound growth rate of 18 percent, increasing from 196,000 departures in
1957 to 871,000 in 1966 according to FAA
data. During this same period, such operations
have grown from 3.0 percent to 4.8 percent of
itinerant movements at FAA tower airports.
The overall growth rate has varied around the
18 percent value cited above, and is projected
to increase at a very slightly moderating pace.
The forecast levels of IFR movements are as
follows:

General Aviation IFR Movements

Year	Number	% of Itinerant Movements
1967	1,027,000	2.0%
1975	3,783,000	4.5%
1980	7,944,000	6.7%

This indicates a growth in the IFR movement
percentage of total (at both tower and non-
tower airports) movements from 2.0% in 1967
to 6.7% in 1980. A movement is here defined
as a take-off or a landing.

In the second report undertaken in 1969,
the previous analysis of movements was reviewed and analyzed in conjunction with a
study of airport activity as recorded on an FAA
tape of Form 29A data on 10,894 airports.
This study confirmed the results of prior results, and used in conjunction with the analysis
of flight hours, produced the analysis of 1968
movements by category of aircraft as presented
in Figure 45.

The data processing of the 29A tape was
further used to determine total movements by
state as shown in Figure 46.

Figure 44

GENERAL AVIATION
ESTIMATE OF MOVEMENTS BY AIRCRAFT TYPE
1967-1980

Type of Aircraft	Annual Movements Per Aircraft		
	1967/68	1975	1980
Single Engine 1-3 Place Reciprocating	1,100	1,300	1,400
Single Engine 4+ Place Reciprocating	650	750	800
Multi-Engine to 12,500 lbs. Up To 600 H.P. Reciprocating	500	550	550
Multi-Engine to 12,500 lbs. Over 600 H.P. Reciprocating	600	650	700
Multi-Engine Over 12,500 lbs. Reciprocating	600	550	500
Multi-Engine Under 12,500 lbs. Turboprop	1,000	1,200	1,300
Multi-Engine Over 12,500 lbs. Turboprop	900	900	900
Multi-Engine Turbojet	600	600	650
Rotorcraft — All	1,500	1,400	1,350
Unspecified	400	400	400
Average Annual Movements — All Types	802	900	929

Source: SPEAS Analysis

Figure 45

GENERAL AVIATION AIRCRAFT
ESTIMATED ANNUAL MOVEMENTS BY TYPE
1967-1980

Type of Aircraft	Millions of Annual Movements			
	1967[2]	1968[2]	1975	1980
Single Engine 1-3 Place Reciprocating	45.9	49.1	72.0	82.2
Single Engine 4+ Place Reciprocating	39.9	42.3	73.7	115.1
Multi-Engine to 12,500 lbs. Up To 600 H.P. Reciprocating	5.2	5.7	10.7	14.3
Multi-Engine to 12,500 lbs. Over 600 H.P. Reciprocating	1.7	1.8	4.0	6.1
Multi-Engine Over 12,500 lbs. Reciprocating	.7	.7	.4	.3
Multi-Engine Under 12,500 lbs. Turboprop	.5	.8	2.9	6.2
Multi-Engine Over 12,500 lbs. Turboprop	.3	.3	.9	1.7
Multi-Engine Turbojet	.5	.6	1.6	3.2
Rotorcraft — All	2.8	3.2	5.9	11.7
Unspecified	.5	.5	.7	.8
Average Annual Movements — All Types	98.0	105.0	172.8	241.6

[1]Calendar Year End
[2]Reflecting SPEAS Adjustment of FAA Data.
Note: A movement is a take-off or a landing.
Source SPEAS Analysis

Figure 46

AIRCRAFT MOVEMENTS
ANALYSIS OF 1968 TOTALS BY STATE
MILLIONS OF MOVEMENTS

Alabama	1.49
Alaska	1.22
Arizona	1.68
Arkansas	.96
California	15.26
Colorado	2.13
Connecticut	.77
Delaware	.34
Florida	6.66
Georgia	2.58
Hawaii	.31
Idaho	.80
Illinois	5.09
Indiana	2.66
Iowa	1.64
Kansas	2.10
Kentucky	1.23
Louisiana	1.75
Maine	.18
Maryland	1.14
Massachusetts	1.64
Michigan	4.36
Minnesota	2.65
Mississippi	1.37
Missouri	2.32
Montana	.89
Nebraska	1.13
Nevada	.99
New Hampshire	.35
New Jersey	2.69
New Mexico	.84
New York	3.93
North Carolina	1.92
North Dakota	.55
Ohio	3.86
Oklahoma	2.65
Oregon	1.57
Pennsylvania	3.06
Rhode Island	.24
South Carolina	.92
South Dakota	.54
Tennessee	1.56
Texas	6.82
Utah	.72
Vermont	.15
Virginia	1.61
Washington	2.68
West Virginia	.59
Wisconsin	2.04
Wyoming	.37
Total United States	105.00

Source: FAA data and
        SPEAS Analysis.

CHAPTER SIX

ACTIVE AIRMEN

An analysis of the history and forecast of the pilot population is presented in Figure 47. This shows active airmen certificates by general type (student, private, commercial, ATR, and other), by year from 1957 to 1980. The total population is forecast to increase by 129 percent from 1967 to 1980, which compares with the active aircraft increase of 112 percent.

Evaluation of several parameters indicated that the relationship of total active airmen to active General Aviation aircraft provides the most reasonable basis for forecasting the pilot population. The trend of this ratio for the ten-year period from 1957 to 1967 has been increasing modestly, and this increase is forecast to continue to 1980. At December 31, 1967 the ratio of total active airmen to total active aircraft, as defined herein, stood at 5.05, and this is forecast to grow to 5.45 by 1980.

The student population has shown the most sensitive response to economic conditions. Assuming stable economic conditions through 1980, it is forecast that the ratio of student to total airmen, which has climbed from a low of 26.2 percent in 1962 to 29.3 percent in 1967, will continue to increase to 32.5 percent in 1980. The reasonableness of this assumption is borne out by the fact that the ratio of non-students to active aircraft, which has exhibited a slight overall upward tendency during the past ten years, continues this trend from 3.57 in 1967 to 3.67 in 1980.

It is assumed that student starts, which went from a low of 61 percent of active students in 1961 to a high of 70 percent in 1964 as the country came out of an economic slowdown, have stabilized at the 68 percent achieved in 1965. This indicates student starts of 123,000, 218,000, and 313,000 in 1967, 1975, and 1980, respectively.

The distribution of certificates among the non-student categories has been relatively constant over the past ten years, and it is assumed

Figure 47

ACTIVE AIRMEN
ANALYSIS BY YEAR BY CLASS OF CERTIFICATE

Year	Students	Private	Commercial	ATR	Other	Total
1957	98,498	124,799	70,813	13,964	1,138	309,212
1958	103,456	140,573	93,126	15,840	1,370	354,365
1959	107,815	139,804	93,815	16,950	1,491	359,875
1960	99,182	138,869	89,904	18,279	1,828	348,062
1961	93,973	144,312	92,976	19,155	2,444	352,860
1962	95,870	149,405	96,047	20,032	4,617	365,971
1963	105,298	152,209	96,341	20,269	4,583	378,700
1964	120,743	175,574	108,428	21,572	4,724	431,041
1965	139,172	196,393	116,665	22,440	6,100	479,770
1966	164,536	205,787	119,854	21,760	6,500(E)	518,437
1967	181,287	253,312	150,135	25,817	7,380	617,098
1968	209,406	278,260	164,458	28,607	10,964	691,695
1975	320,000	403,000	243,000	41,000	10,000	1,017,000
1980	460,000	552,000	332,000	57,000	14,000	1,415,000

Source: FAA Statistical Handbook of Aviation and SPEAS Analysis

that this relationship will remain through 1980. Confirmation of one of these elements is provided by relating forecast ATRs to air carrier departures. The forecast relationship through to 1980, shows the same relative stability that has been observed since 1960.

Instrument ratings have been a rather constant 20 percent of total active certificates since 1961, and it is forecast that this relationship will also continue. This indicates a growth from the 122,043 at December 31, 1967 to 203,000 in 1975, and 283,000 in 1980.

The preceding analysis and forecasts were published in the initial report prepared in 1968. Year end 1968 figures subsequently made available for the total number of airmen in the United States by class of certificate indicate an overall growth of 11.9 percent during the calendar year 1968. The greatest absolute growth occurred in the student category, which showed a growth of 15.5 percent as licensed pilots entered training schools to upgrade their ratings under the GI Bill. In other categories,

private certificates increased by 9.8 percent and commercials by 9.5 percent.

The historical relationships of total airmen to aircraft by state were determined, and from these and examination of 1967 and 1968 ratios both by state and by SMSA, the trends of these relationships were forecast to 1980. Similarly, the past mix of certificates within the states and SMSAs were used to project mixes for 1975 and 1980. The resulting analyses of active airmen by class of certificate by state and by SMSAs are presented in Figures 48 and 49 respectively.

This shows that 51 percent of all active airmen are within these metropolitan areas, as opposed to 44 percent of the active aircraft. The major categories of student, private and commercial licenses all have approximately 50 percent of their number in these SMSAs. As is to be expected because of the basing practices of airlines to locate pilots near major hubs, 75 percent of all ATRs are within the 75 areas.

(Figures 48 and 49 follow)

Figure 48

ACTIVE AIRMEN BY STATE

ANALYSIS BY YEAR BY CLASS OF CERTIFICATE

State	Year	Student	Private	Commercial	ATR	Other	Total
Alabama	1967	2,569	3,186	2,404	141	175	8,475
	1968	2,841	3,609	2,706	166	189	9,511
	1975	3,856	4,960	3,150	211	223	12,400
	1980	5,311	6,780	4,075	284	250	16,700
Alaska	1967	1,474	1,464	818	136	9	3,901
	1968	1,917	1,768	1,000	158	16	4,859
	1975	2,381	2,363	1,323	202	31	6,300
	1980	3,062	3,037	1,701	243	57	8,100
Arizona	1967	2,247	3,496	2,068	166	63	8,040
	1968	2,830	3,783	2,342	195	84	9,234
	1975	3,670	5,525	3,137	254	114	12,700
	1980	4,479	6,742	3,829	295	155	15,500
Arkansas	1967	1,696	2,269	1,460	49	32	5,506
	1968	1,952	2,479	1,591	61	43	6,126
	1975	3,799	4,913	3,170	121	97	12,100
	1980	4,897	6,191	4,019	154	139	15,400
California	1967	25,210	38,816	21,291	4,456	1,343	91,116
	1968	28,858	42,475	23,540	5,001	1,736	101,610
	1975	39,227	59,896	32,900	6,468	2,109	140,600
	1980	52,752	80,258	44,086	8,478	2,826	188,400
Colorado	1967	3,498	4,699	3,043	745	99	12,084
	1968	4,278	5,206	3,363	813	152	13,812
	1975	5,577	7,487	4,803	1,051	182	19,100
	1980	7,247	9,613	6,149	1,147	244	24,400
Connecticut	1967	2,493	2,740	1,804	638	87	7,762
	1968	2,832	3,037	1,962	705	101	8,637
	1975	3,718	3,989	2,554	915	124	11,300
	1980	4,995	5,295	3,330	1,215	165	15,000
Delaware	1967	405	580	333	67	15	1,400
	1968	495	651	381	74	17	1,618
	1975	861	1,201	670	136	32	2,900
	1980	1,264	1,739	958	193	46	4,200

(Continued on Next Page)

Figure 48

(Continued from Preceding Page)

State	Year	Student	Private	Commercial	ATR	Other	Total
D. C.	1967	297	624	553	85	39	1,598
	1968	342	599	538	82	53	1,614
	1975	560	1,092	939	133	76	2,800
	1980	800	1,560	1,344	200	96	4,000
Florida	1967	8,675	9,750	8,824	2,217	366	29,832
	1968	9,703	10,613	9,777	2,416	447	32,956
	1975	13,827	15,498	13,734	2,784	557	46,400
	1980	19,746	22,107	19,418	3,542	787	65,600
Georgia	1967	4,117	4,163	3,203	995	113	12,591
	1968	4,969	4,718	3,528	1,116	157	14,488
	1975	7,829	7,968	5,592	1,701	210	23,300
	1980	12,210	12,352	8,354	2,463	321	35,700
Hawaii	1967	549	370	432	117	16	1,484
	1968	609	440	517	152	26	1,744
	1975	878	622	698	166	36	2,400
	1980	1,739	1,264	1,368	277	52	4,700
Idaho	1967	944	1,753	969	64	24	3,754
	1968	1,134	1,856	1,051	72	28	4,141
	1975	1,566	2,802	1,488	96	48	6,000
	1980	2,304	3,978	2,023	127	68	8,500
Illinois	1967	9,112	13,186	6,669	1,502	482	30,951
	1968	10,246	14,325	7,246	1,694	512	34,023
	1975	16,120	22,504	11,278	2,500	798	53,200
	1980	23,360	31,752	15,876	3,478	1,134	75,600
Indiana	1967	4,664	6,930	2,899	242	85	14,820
	1968	5,243	7,549	3,161	271	101	16,325
	1975	7,466	11,020	4,693	379	142	23,700
	1980	10,833	16,008	6,900	552	207	34,500
Iowa	1967	3,043	5,395	2,206	72	59	10,775
	1968	3,577	5,931	2,395	79	64	12,046
	1975	4,263	7,169	2,978	102	88	14,600
	1980	6,946	11,063	4,669	161	161	23,000
Kansas	1967	3,564	6,477	3,078	380	71	13,570
	1968	4,076	6,932	3,350	427	84	14,869
	1975	6,152	10,714	5,085	590	159	22,700
	1980	8,535	14,337	6,815	767	246	30,700

(Continued on Next Page)

Figure 48

(Continued from Preceding Page)

State	Year	Student	Private	Commercial	ATR	Other	Total
Kentucky	1967	1,614	2,239	1,165	73	51	5,142
	1968	2,078	2,441	1,282	77	62	5,940
	1975	2,512	3,480	1,808	112	88	8,000
	1980	3,517	4,872	2,531	157	123	11,200
Louisiana	1967	2,500	2,919	2,367	246	81	8,113
	1968	3,100	3,399	2,610	274	96	9,479
	1975	5,023	5,925	4,540	435	177	16,100
	1980	7,536	8,976	6,624	600	264	24,000
Maine	1967	841	999	665	30	28	2,563
	1968	977	1,053	710	37	34	2,811
	1975	1,416	1,638	1,050	50	46	4,200
	1980	1,915	2,184	1,372	67	62	5,600
Maryland	1967	2,304	2,871	1,468	228	95	6,966
	1968	2,782	3,266	1,645	265	121	8,079
	1975	6,620	8,180	4,220	700	280	20,000
	1980	11,254	13,872	7,174	1,224	476	34,000
Massachusetts	1967	3,276	3,934	2,816	475	151	10,652
	1968	3,876	4,367	3,023	536	183	11,985
	1975	5,759	6,882	4,710	791	258	18,400
	1980	7,843	9,387	6,275	1,046	349	24,900
Michigan	1967	6,885	9,530	4,297	580	167	21,459
	1968	8,092	10,748	4,573	598	203	24,214
	1975	10,987	14,683	6,720	907	303	33,600
	1980	15,015	19,747	9,100	1,229	409	45,500
Minnesota	1967	4,310	6,875	3,513	673	119	15,490
	1968	5,123	7,562	3,853	751	140	17,429
	1975	7,382	11,318	5,879	1,114	207	25,900
	1980	10,109	15,233	7,968	1,509	281	35,100
Mississippi	1967	1,739	1,844	1,341	49	55	5,028
	1968	1,939	2,083	1,418	60	55	5,555
	1975	2,647	2,798	1,898	75	82	7,500
	1980	3,834	4,071	2,668	108	119	10,800
Missouri	1967	4,543	6,664	3,395	547	122	15,271
	1968	5,080	7,394	3,745	604	145	16,968
	1975	7,925	11,111	5,750	881	233	25,900
	1980	11,186	15,457	8,036	1,195	326	36,200

(Continued on Next Page)

Figure 48

(Continued from Preceding Page)

State	Year	Student	Private	Commercial	ATR	Other	Total
Montana	1967	1,417	2,237	1,163	46	18	4,881
	1968	1,563	2,415	1,225	50	21	5,274
	1975	2,348	3,531	1,825	63	33	7,800
	1980	3,352	5,017	2,586	89	56	11,100
Nebraska	1967	1,767	3,176	1,576	58	32	6,609
	1968	2,037	3,442	1,667	69	35	7,250
	1975	3,358	5,843	2,927	110	62	12,300
	1980	4,830	8,260	4,165	157	88	17,500
Nevada	1967	963	1,228	668	70	17	2,946
	1968	1,069	1,303	776	82	24	3,254
	1975	1,744	2,226	1,171	122	37	5,300
	1980	2,549	3,249	1,671	169	62	7,700
New Hampshire	1967	580	727	569	172	33	2,081
	1968	614	821	608	188	32	2,263
	1975	1,004	1,264	983	295	54	3,600
	1980	1,405	1,755	1,365	405	70	5,000
New Jersey	1967	4,625	5,811	3,892	1,340	203	15,871
	1968	5,817	6,412	4,315	1,472	257	18,273
	1975	9,720	11,891	7,873	2,495	421	32,400
	1980	14,440	17,433	11,495	3,515	617	47,500
New Mexico	1967	1,539	2,562	1,185	56	38	5,380
	1968	1,687	2,733	1,327	63	53	5,863
	1975	2,554	4,237	1,931	107	71	8,900
	1980	3,456	5,712	2,580	156	96	12,000
New York	1967	9,480	11,632	7,719	1,959	477	31,267
	1968	10,684	12,750	8,222	2,075	581	34,312
	1975	16,714	20,714	13,536	3,014	822	54,800
	1980	23,317	29,108	18,822	3,810	1,143	76,200
North Carolina	1967	3,162	3,681	2,470	235	117	9,665
	1968	3,790	4,003	2,651	250	131	10,825
	1975	6,012	6,912	4,428	432	216	18,000
	1980	9,126	10,422	6,480	648	324	27,000
North Dakota	1967	1,113	1,220	796	16	14	3,159
	1968	1,331	1,444	897	19	16	3,707
	1975	2,136	2,328	1,476	30	30	6,000
	1980	3,294	3,579	2,226	46	55	9,200

(Continued on Next Page)

Figure 48
(Continued from Preceding Page)

State	Year	Student	Private	Commercial	ATR	Other	Total
Ohio	1967	8,244	12,105	5,817	472	301	26,939
	1968	9,422	13,170	6,256	536	335	29,719
	1975	12,782	18,372	8,795	699	452	41,100
	1980	16,536	23,638	11,342	901	583	53,000
Oklahoma	1967	3,451	5,153	3,022	354	172	12,152
	1968	3,856	5,670	3,281	379	180	13,366
	1975	6,307	9,158	5,249	583	303	21,600
	1980	8,378	12,070	6,788	767	397	28,400
Oregon	1967	2,691	4,709	2,070	95	65	9,630
	1968	2,983	5,016	2,267	113	76	10,455
	1975	3,947	6,191	2,825	132	105	13,200
	1980	5,716	8,492	3,959	185	148	18,500
Pennsylvania	1967	6,258	8,689	5,272	655	253	21,127
	1968	7,313	9,483	5,655	733	302	23,486
	1975	10,226	13,954	8,482	1,128	410	34,200
	1980	14,180	18,907	11,560	1,591	562	46,800
Rhode Island	1967	352	499	404	38	28	1,321
	1968	444	535	445	48	26	1,498
	1975	532	766	604	58	40	2,000
	1980	772	1,119	870	84	55	2,900
South Carolina	1967	1,474	1,590	1,343	94	41	4,542
	1968	1,784	1,806	1,505	106	49	5,250
	1975	3,366	3,495	2,732	208	99	9,900
	1980	5,725	5,874	4,389	347	165	16,500
South Dakota	1967	864	1,549	748	27	32	3,220
	1968	1,041	1,608	806	27	29	3,511
	1975	1,650	2,844	1,392	54	60	6,000
	1980	2,455	4,127	2,042	88	88	8,800
Tennessee	1967	2,674	3,497	2,110	273	70	8,624
	1968	3,068	3,988	2,374	306	83	9,819
	1975	4,038	5,276	3,070	400	116	12,900
	1980	5,796	7,562	4,324	552	166	18,400
Texas	1967	12,149	18,117	12,336	2,117	448	45,167
	1968	14,013	19,931	13,479	2,318	585	50,326
	1975	21,762	31,824	20,280	3,354	780	78,000
	1980	30,495	43,977	27,071	4,387	1,070	107,000

(Continued on Next Page)

Figure 48

(Continued from Preceding Page)

State	Year	Student	Private	Commercial	ATR	Other	Total
Utah	1967	1,096	1,933	998	101	33	4,161
	1968	1,218	2,094	1,065	94	42	4,513
	1975	2,484	4,232	2,199	202	83	9,200
	1980	3,795	6,233	3,261	288	123	13,700
Vermont	1967	284	383	269	12	11	959
	1968	350	422	276	21	10	1,079
	1975	416	559	389	21	15	1,400
	1980	596	798	552	32	22	2,000
Virginia	1967	3,000	3,639	3,107	733	167	10,646
	1968	3,533	4,157	3,409	801	205	12,105
	1975	5,281	6,366	5,281	1,178	294	18,400
	1980	7,857	9,396	7,668	1,647	432	27,000
Washington	1967	4,953	6,947	4,279	734	249	17,162
	1968	5,705	7,676	4,818	844	339	19,382
	1975	7,163	10,053	6,052	1,037	395	24,700
	1980	8,905	12,485	7,466	1,254	490	30,600
West Virginia	1967	707	979	640	33	26	2,385
	1968	798	1,032	684	36	29	2,579
	1975	1,247	1,701	1,126	76	50	4,200
	1980	1,836	2,440	1,635	116	73	6,100
Wisconsin	1967	3,207	4,813	2,190	183	105	10,498
	1968	3,767	5,358	2,420	224	120	11,889
	1975	4,975	7,325	3,365	258	177	16,100
	1980	6,552	9,492	4,389	336	231	21,000
Wyoming	1967	523	1,070	514	19	17	2,143
	1968	606	1,049	535	23	17	2,230
	1975	783	1,360	708	23	26	2,900
	1980	1,053	1,744	935	30	38	3,800
Total	1967	181,287	253,312	150,135	25,817	7,380	617,931
	1968	209,406	278,260	164,458	28,607	10,964	691,695
	1975	304,580	418,170	243,486	38,963	11,801	1,017,000
	1980	429,105	580,764	336,303	52,311	16,517	1,415,000

Source: FAA Historical data and SPEAS forecast.

Figure 49

ACTIVE AIRMEN BY SMSA
ANALYSIS BY YEAR BY CLASS OF CERTIFICATE

SMSA	Year	Student	Private	Commercial	ATR	Other	Total
New York	1967	4,785	5,920	4,566	1,575	209	17,055
	1968	5,504	6,455	4,752	1,635	236	18,582
	1975	9,445	11,130	8,109	2,735	381	31,800
	1980	12,558	14,784	10,668	3,528	462	42,000
Chicago	1967	5,038	7,041	3,824	1,321	357	17,581
	1968	5,761	7,714	4,173	1,453	365	19,466
	1975	9,060	11,850	6,360	2,160	570	30,000
	1980	9,425	12,096	6,447	2,149	583	30,700
Los Angeles	1967	7,494	13,082	6,904	1,556	480	29,516
	1968	8,253	14,052	7,398	1,618	538	31,859
	1975	13,000	22,100	11,500	2,550	850	50,000
	1980	17,382	29,504	15,185	3,397	1,132	66,600
Philadelphia	1967	2,441	3,284	1,894	231	104	7,954
	1968	2,890	3,566	2,034	282	123	8,895
	1975	5,120	6,320	3,618	521	221	15,800
	1980	7,670	9,416	5,404	803	307	23,600
Detroit	1967	2,681	3,725	1,752	320	83	8,561
	1968	3,130	4,135	1,852	312	90	9,519
	1975	5,810	7,543	3,412	578	157	17,500
	1980	7,926	10,186	4,665	785	238	23,800
Boston	1967	1,879	2,265	1,631	339	103	6,217
	1968	2,242	2,521	1,762	366	112	7,003
	1975	3,628	4,102	2,825	576	169	11,300
	1980	4,992	5,725	3,869	780	234	15,600
San Francisco	1967	3,454	5,419	3,293	1,037	193	13,396
	1968	3,924	5,896	3,643	1,221	226	14,910
	1975	7,182	10,759	6,585	2,168	406	27,100
	1980	10,679	16,080	9,753	3,143	645	40,300
Pittsburgh	1967	1,381	1,616	1,152	264	51	4,464
	1968	1,646	1,773	1,286	281	50	5,036
	1975	2,681	2,895	2,083	459	82	8,200
	1980	4,414	4,779	3,416	756	135	13,500

(Continued on Next Page)

Figure 49

(Continued from Preceding Page)

SMSA	Year	Student	Private	Commercial	ATR	Other	Total
St. Louis	1967	1,744	2,885	1,417	237	53	6,336
	1968	2,043	3,015	1,570	267	61	6,956
	1975	3,545	5,837	2,842	474	102	12,800
	1980	5,153	8,500	4,092	688	167	18,600
Washington, D.C.	1967	2,332	2,954	2,427	729	153	8,595
	1968	2,306	3,266	2,548	734	179	9,033
	1975	5,211	6,678	5,423	1,621	367	19,300
	1980	8,743	11,310	9,100	2,697	650	32,500
Cleveland	1967	1,505	2,003	1,047	101	39	4,695
	1968	1,695	2,197	1,123	112	42	5,169
	1975	2,886	3,749	1,901	194	70	8,800
	1980	3,826	4,996	2,516	257	105	11,700
Baltimore	1967	660	1,195	573	83	27	2,583
	1968	1,037	1,487	619	88	28	3,259
	1975	2,192	3,940	1,890	286	92	8,400
	1980	3,799	6,772	3,248	507	174	14,500
Newark	1967	1,048	1,506	1,002	350	62	3,963
	1968	1,219	1,618	975	371	66	4,249
	1975	2,154	2,812	1,687	629	118	7,400
	1980	2,891	3,714	2,225	813	157	9,800
Minn./St. Paul	1967	2,197	3,493	1,904	555	66	8,215
	1968	2,639	3,844	2,110	609	75	9,277
	1975	4,885	7,138	3,887	1,152	138	17,200
	1980	6,877	10,109	5,467	1,628	219	24,300
Houston	1967	1,906	2,634	1,480	405	30	6,455
	1968	2,167	3,069	1,698	454	48	7,436
	1975	3,785	5,330	2,922	772	91	12,900
	1980	5,161	7,359	3,995	1,043	142	17,700
Buffalo	1967	746	938	531	79	34	2,327
	1968	826	1,056	590	88	42	2,602
	1975	1,336	1,709	949	139	67	4,200
	1980	1,659	2,122	1,170	166	83	5,200
Milwaukee	1967	1,034	1,518	659	46	47	3,304
	1968	1,146	1,702	743	55	50	3,696
	1975	2,133	3,174	1,387	103	103	6,900
	1980	3,100	4,610	2,010	130	150	10,000

(Continued on Next Page)

Figure 49

(Continued from Preceding Page)

SMSA	Year	Student	Private	Commercial	ATR	Other	Total
Cincinnati	1967	734	1,263	637	61	64	2,759
	1968	857	1,352	678	63	61	3,011
	1975	1,459	2,295	1,142	102	102	5,100
	1980	1,722	2,706	1,338	114	120	6,000
Paterson	1967	954	1,238	817	344	52	3,405
	1968	1,138	1,403	921	381	57	3,900
	1975	2,549	3,141	2,044	835	131	8,700
	1980	4,572	5,611	3,627	1,457	233	15,500
Dallas	1967	1,842	2,811	1,796	814	93	7,356
	1968	2,172	3,105	1,975	890	105	8,247
	1975	3,537	5,079	3,203	1,394	187	13,400
	1980	5,486	7,887	4,947	2,070	310	20,700
Seattle	1967	2,494	3,018	2,139	620	140	8,411
	1968	2,868	3,501	2,407	700	164	9,640
	1975	4,351	5,315	3,635	1,051	248	14,600
	1980	6,159	7,519	5,109	1,463	350	20,600
Kansas City	1967	1,694	2,601	1,525	516	64	6,400
	1968	1,948	3,049	1,666	594	67	7,324
	1975	3,257	5,100	2,757	964	122	12,200
	1980	5,038	7,896	4,230	1,448	188	18,800
San Diego	1967	1,581	2,579	1,616	151	117	6,044
	1968	1,927	2,898	1,921	170	130	7,046
	1975	2,959	4,450	2,938	259	194	10,800
	1980	4,411	6,649	4,363	387	290	16,100
Atlanta	1967	1,812	1,917	1,432	849	46	6,116
	1968	2,023	2,191	1,571	925	55	6,765
	1975	3,930	4,258	3,039	1,768	105	13,100
	1980	6,840	7,433	5,290	3,032	205	22,800
Indianapolis	1967	1,042	1,558	640	110	22	3,372
	1968	1,146	1,691	706	122	25	3,690
	1975	2,184	3,199	1,337	231	49	7,000
	1980	3,067	4,469	1,872	323	69	9,800
Miami	1967	2,420	2,233	3,163	1,696	207	9,719
	1968	2,423	2,310	3,404	1,781	202	10,120
	1975	4,588	4,324	6,298	3,252	338	18,800
	1980	7,007	6,664	9,552	4,891	486	28,600

(Continued on Next Page)

Figure 49

(Continued from Preceding Page)

SMSA	Year	Student	Private	Commercial	ATR	Other	Total
Denver	1967	1,769	2,641	1,917	695	59	7,081
	1968	2,136	2,935	2,079	745	58	7,953
	1975	3,132	4,304	3,004	1,067	93	11,600
	1980	3,862	5,297	3,649	1,264	128	14,200
New Orleans	1967	585	733	636	161	24	2,139
	1968	691	780	687	172	26	2,356
	1975	915	1,029	899	223	34	3,100
	1980	1,551	1,698	1,433	362	56	5,100
Portland	1967	1,147	2,000	934	67	28	4,176
	1968	1,250	2,136	1,006	75	31	4,498
	1975	2,176	3,705	1,739	125	55	7,800
	1980	3,348	5,700	2,664	192	96	12,000
San Bernardino	1967	1,487	2,025	1,128	98	42	4,780
	1968	1,742	2,312	1,252	105	52	5,463
	1975	2,640	3,519	1,892	166	83	8,300
	1980	3,593	4,803	2,565	226	113	11,300
Tampa	1967	846	1,113	917	43	19	2,938
	1968	923	1,243	1,000	56	31	3,253
	1975	1,751	2,324	1,860	104	61	6,100
	1980	2,929	3,838	3,060	172	101	10,100
Columbus	1967	841	1,240	697	93	41	2,912
	1968	933	1,399	756	108	48	3,244
	1975	2,008	2,967	1,594	228	103	6,900
	1980	3,215	4,676	2,496	360	153	10,900
Rochester	1967	579	762	402	24	45	1,812
	1968	629	850	413	24	54	1,970
	1975	1,384	1,858	894	52	112	4,300
	1980	2,229	2,988	1,428	83	172	6,900
Dayton	1967	845	1,318	626	59	31	2,879
	1968	1,033	1,427	668	56	44	3,228
	1975	1,760	2,436	1,133	94	77	5,500
	1980	2,624	3,641	1,681	139	115	8,200
Louisville	1967	475	760	388	21	19	1,663
	1968	626	827	456	22	24	1,955
	1975	1,024	1,356	742	39	39	3,200
	1980	1,536	2,040	1,110	57	57	4,800

(Continued on Next Page)

Figure 49

(Continued from Preceding Page)

SMSA	Year	Student	Private	Commercial	ATR	Other	Total
Birmingham	1967	412	619	415	34	11	1,491
	1968	463	696	460	37	11	1,667
	1975	949	1,425	928	71	27	3,400
	1980	1,344	2,016	1,301	96	43	4,800
Providence	1967	284	405	266	28	19	1,002
	1968	358	432	306	34	18	1,148
	1975	525	641	456	51	27	1,700
	1980	553	680	484	54	29	1,800
San Antonio	1967	612	965	951	120	27	2,675
	1968	811	1,063	1,028	124	31	3,057
	1975	1,277	1,680	1,603	192	48	4,800
	1980	1,495	1,971	1,854	218	62	5,600
Anaheim	1967	1,797	2,343	1,408	339	121	6,008
	1968	2,240	2,774	1,617	411	144	7,186
	1975	4,747	5,897	3,414	853	289	15,200
	1980	7,817	9,562	5,516	1,360	445	24,700
Hartford	1967	666	802	484	43	22	2,017
	1968	763	871	528	51	25	2,238
	1975	1,372	1,560	940	84	44	4,000
	1980	2,236	2,542	1,521	130	71	6,500
Memphis	1967	743	1,019	36	99	19	1,916
	1968	876	1,171	742	111	19	2,919
	1975	1,450	1,934	1,214	168	34	4,800
	1980	2,364	3,159	1,958	257	62	7,800
Phoenix	1967	1,326	2,113	1,275	129	43	4,886
	1968	1,688	2,300	1,485	155	52	5,680
	1975	2,563	3,500	2,236	224	77	8,600
	1980	3,267	4,499	2,849	275	110	11,000
New Haven	1967	435	465	300	42	14	1,256
	1968	528	525	313	41	13	1,420
	1975	973	960	569	75	23	2,600
	1980	1,313	1,288	763	101	35	3,500
Albany	1967	401	531	295	26	35	1,288
	1968	471	593	323	26	35	1,448
	1975	975	1,233	666	54	72	3,000
	1980	1,592	2,019	1,083	93	113	4,900

(Continued on Next Page)

Figure 49

(Continued from Preceding Page)

SMSA	Year	Student	Private	Commercial	ATR	Other	Total
Bridgeport	1967	760	837	684	494	36	2,811
	1968	875	930	745	544	39	3,133
	1975	1,472	1,555	1,232	879	62	5,200
	1980	1,732	1,842	1,440	1,007	79	6,100
San Jose	1967	1,880	2,548	1,472	711	86	6,697
	1968	1,951	2,809	1,652	759	101	7,272
	1975	4,033	5,777	3,664	1,518	208	15,200
	1980	6,480	9,243	5,361	2,359	357	23,800
Toledo	1967	485	662	311	31	15	1,504
	1968	569	744	335	36	17	1,701
	1975	873	1,139	510	52	26	2,600
	1980	1,277	1,668	741	76	38	3,800
Sacramento	1967	1,088	1,731	866	89	31	3,805
	1968	1,299	1,830	995	100	28	4,252
	1975	2,631	3,692	2,010	198	69	8,600
	1980	4,313	6,067	3,281	311	128	14,100
Jersey City	1967	146	154	117	17	8	442
	1968	182	156	126	17	6	487
	1975	413	353	284	37	13	1,100
	1980	451	386	308	40	15	1,200
Akron	1967	456	811	332	32	22	1,653
	1968	551	831	387	36	24	1,829
	1975	876	1,319	612	55	38	2,900
	1980	1,238	1,870	861	78	53	4,100
Worcester	1967	397	521	267	17	7	1,209
	1968	466	549	276	23	11	1,325
	1975	671	789	393	32	15	1,900
	1980	915	1,082	536	44	23	2,600
Norfolk	1967	128	318	258	31	15	750
	1968	130	296	246	33	18	723
	1975	233	546	442	52	27	1,300
	1980	262	582	470	55	31	1,400
Gary	1967	405	556	216	16	5	1,198
	1968	444	630	230	17	6	1,327
	1975	804	1,142	413	29	12	2,400
	1980	1,236	1,765	633	44	22	3,700

(Continued on Next Page)

Figure 49

(Continued from Preceding Page)

SMSA	Year	Student	Private	Commercial	ATR	Other	Total
Fort Worth	1967	1,086	1,574	1,193	430	54	4,337
	1968	1,161	1,807	1,352	462	65	4,847
	1975	1,791	2,775	2,050	638	96	7,400
	1980	2,294	3,544	2,585	855	122	9,400
Syracuse	1967	473	602	346	35	7	1,463
	1968	505	638	363	36	5	1,548
	1975	951	1,198	673	64	14	2,900
	1980	1,184	1,490	828	76	22	3,600
Springfield	1967	341	440	312	28	8	1,129
	1968	422	492	323	35	8	1,280
	1975	926	1,081	700	76	17	2,800
	1980	1,195	1,396	893	94	22	3,600
Greensboro	1967	535	637	372	75	18	1,637
	1968	669	723	400	81	21	1,894
	1975	1,314	1,413	777	155	41	3,700
	1980	2,385	2,566	1,400	275	74	6,700
Oklahoma City	1967	907	1,416	855	183	58	3,419
	1968	1,014	1,601	905	193	60	3,773
	1975	1,296	2,035	1,147	245	77	4,800
	1980	1,870	2,926	1,642	352	110	6,900
Youngstown	1967	402	542	256	24	15	1,239
	1968	441	589	273	28	14	1,345
	1975	790	1,053	485	48	24	2,400
	1980	1,023	1,364	623	59	31	3,100
Honolulu	1967	384	370	432	117	16	1,319
	1968	399	378	452	135	18	1,382
	1975	555	536	621	165	23	1,900
	1980	852	821	945	247	35	2,900
Allentown	1967	240	469	231	42	17	999
	1968	276	486	273	48	17	1,100
	1975	479	838	471	84	28	1,900
	1980	936	1,628	918	163	55	3,700
Nashville	1967	403	575	331	81	20	1,410
	1968	437	655	390	89	21	1,592
	1975	831	1,236	732	162	39	3,000
	1980	1,256	1,858	1,094	234	58	4,500

(Continued on Next Page)

Figure 49

(*Continued from Preceding Page*)

SMSA	Year	Student	Private	Commercial	ATR	Other	Total
Grand Rapids	1967	434	674	245	19	4	1,376
	1968	503	741	258	23	3	1,528
	1975	955	1,408	485	43	9	2,900
	1980	1,308	1,861	658	58	15	3,900
Omaha	1967	542	927	532	28	13	2,042
	1968	635	1,029	562	31	11	2,268
	1975	927	1,495	815	46	17	3,300
	1980	1,269	2,034	1,107	63	27	4,500
Jacksonville	1967	472	587	609	45	11	1,724
	1968	481	610	667	47	11	1,816
	1975	774	977	1,059	73	17	2,900
	1980	1,049	1,318	1,416	94	23	3,900
Salt Lake City	1967	593	989	566	78	21	2,247
	1968	648	1,080	605	71	25	2,429
	1975	1,197	2,007	1,116	126	54	4,500
	1980	1,662	2,771	1,532	161	74	6,200
Richmond	1967	365	438	253	28	9	1,093
	1968	366	430	248	30	9	1,083
	1975	775	920	529	58	18	2,300
	1980	1,224	1,437	824	86	29	3,600
Tulsa	1967	725	1,163	706	82	61	2,737
	1968	909	1,267	785	82	61	3,104
	1975	1,205	1,677	1,033	107	78	4,100
	1980	1,564	2,173	1,330	138	95	5,300
Flint	1967	393	534	184	14	1	1,126
	1968	482	624	183	14	2	1,305
	1975	742	952	278	22	6	2,000
	1980	1,119	1,422	414	33	12	3,000
Wilmington	1967	291	468	231	58	13	1,061
	1968	360	508	252	63	12	1,195
	1975	912	1,272	627	156	33	3,000
	1980	1,694	2,327	1,138	281	60	5,500
Wichita	1967	927	1,607	836	50	13	3,433
	1968	1,000	1,746	913	51	14	3,724
	1975	1,856	3,236	1,684	97	27	6,900
	1980	2,304	3,986	2,066	110	34	8,500

(*Continued on Next Page*)

Figure 49

(Continued from Preceding Page)

SMSA	Year	Student	Private	Commercial	ATR	Other	Total
Harrisburg	1967	285	411	232	15	8	951
	1968	327	439	253	16	10	1,045
	1975	917	1,215	699	43	26	2,900
	1980	1,871	2,466	1,416	88	59	5,900
Knoxville	1967	292	390	225	27	6	940
	1968	302	442	243	27	9	1,023
	1975	356	520	283	30	11	1,200
	1980	537	781	421	43	18	1,800
Fresno	1967	515	924	403	17	12	1,871
	1968	619	978	438	24	13	2,072
	1975	957	1,514	672	38	19	3,200
	1980	1,170	1,801	756	46	27	3,800
Mobile	1967	246	323	193	11	6	779
	1968	263	362	220	12	6	863
	1975	551	756	455	25	13	1,800
	1980	918	1,263	753	42	24	3,000
Total	1967	87,944	126,808	76,962	19,435	4,131	315,280
	1968	101,777	139,600	85,594	21,088	4,579	351,638
	1975	177,561	242,981	146,507	36,162	7,989	611,200
	1980	256,013	349,051	209,363	51,606	11,567	877,600

Source: FAA Historical data and SPEAS forecast.

CHAPTER SEVEN

PASSENGERS AND CARGO CARRIED

General

Historical information on the volume of passengers and cargo carried by General Aviation has never been collected on a routine basis. On occasion, special studies have been accomplished in the past which provide some insight as regards this traffic. The most meaningful of these have been examined and are commented upon in this report.

1. User Profile

The FAA publishes the only authoritative data on numbers of aircraft and hours of operation in General Aviation by type of use. This information is taken from Form 2350, Use and Inspection report, and indicates only the primary use of each aircraft.

There are a large number of multi-use aircraft, with the largest group being those for which the use is divided between pleasure and business. An extensive direct contact program with active aircraft owners would be required to establish a more detailed analysis of use than that provided by the FAA, and the usefulness of such data is questionable.

The history and forecasts of aircraft and hours flown by type of use are shown in Figure 50. A graphic presentation of this data by use of aircraft is offered in Figure 51.

The forecasts were developed from an evaluation of historical trends and of forecast projections of utilization and numbers of hours and aircraft by use and type. There were variations among the uses, but not of an order of magnitude which would have altered any of the basic relationships. Within the commercial use category, for example, air taxi use is anticipated to experience very strong growth throughout the forecast period, but aerial application is forecast to continue its historically slower than average growth.

Instructional flying is forecast to increase in direct proportion to the increase projected in the population of student airman certificates. Personal flying is projected to increase slightly faster than the total, and business flying slightly slower. The compound growth rates for hours flown are 7.8 percent and 6.9 percent for personal and business flying respectively, and 7.6 percent for all General Aviation flying hours.

2. Volume of Passenger Traffic — Previous Studies

The actual volume of passenger traffic carried in General Aviation aircraft can only be ascertained, in the absence of reliable data, by surveys which set out to define the average number of occupants carried on each flight. Although previous studies are now dated, they are nevertheless useful in providing some historical figures with which to be able to project future average aircraft occupancy. Apart from the SPEAS survey undertaken for this study, there have been three significant earlier studies made of General Aviation passenger volumes.

a) Michigan State Survey (1962 Data)

A study was published in 1963 — the "Michigan Fact Finder Survey" which included statistical data on the number of passengers carried on General Aviation aircraft in the State of Michigan. This study is approximately 7 years old, but it is probably the most extensive survey completed from the standpoint of volume of statistical data. The survey was conducted during all operational hours, for a seven-day period (July 28 through August 3, 1962) at all of the 137 licensed airports in the State. Also, activity at Michigan's unlicensed airports and six military airports was included to the extent that

The Magnitude and Economic Impact of General Aviation — 1968-1980

Figure 50

ANALYSIS OF GENERAL AVIATION USERS
AIRCRAFT AND HOURS FLOWN
1953-1980

AIRCRAFT

Year	Business	Commercial	Instruction	Personal	Other	Total
1953	18,220	7,090	5,440	29,260	1,030	61,040
1954	18,570	7,850	4,720	29,350	690	61,180
1957	21,520	8,800	5,680	29,850	670	66,520
1961	20,728	10,999	6,095	41,706	1,104	80,632
1963	20,793	11,548	6,121	44,860	1,766	85,088
1964	21,127	11,979	6,855	46,721	2,060	88,742
1965	21,650	11,355	8,034	51,093	3,310	95,442
1967*	30,100	14,449	14,155	62,540	956	122,200
1980	58,435	29,415	30,616	139,510	2,024	260,000

HOURS FLOWN IN THOUSANDS

Year	Business	Commercial	Instruction	Personal	Other	Total
1953	3,626	1,649	1,248	1,846	158	8,527
1954	3,875	1,829	1,292	1,920	47	8,963
1957	4,864	2,013	1,864	2,109	88	10,938
1961	5,699	2,634	1,796	3,398	75	13,602
1963	5,740	3,172	2,417	3,626	151	15,106
1964	5,823	3,305	2,675	3,777	158	15,738
1965	5,857	3,348	3,346	4,016	166	16,733
1967*	8,483	4,353	5,916	5,470	223	24,445
1980	20,277	13,237	14,910	14,578	579	63,581

*FAA data adjusted to include all Active Aircraft as defined herein.

Source: FAA Statistical Handbooks of Aviation and SPEAS analysis.

Figure 51
GENERAL AVIATION AIRCRAFT BY USE
(1953-1980)

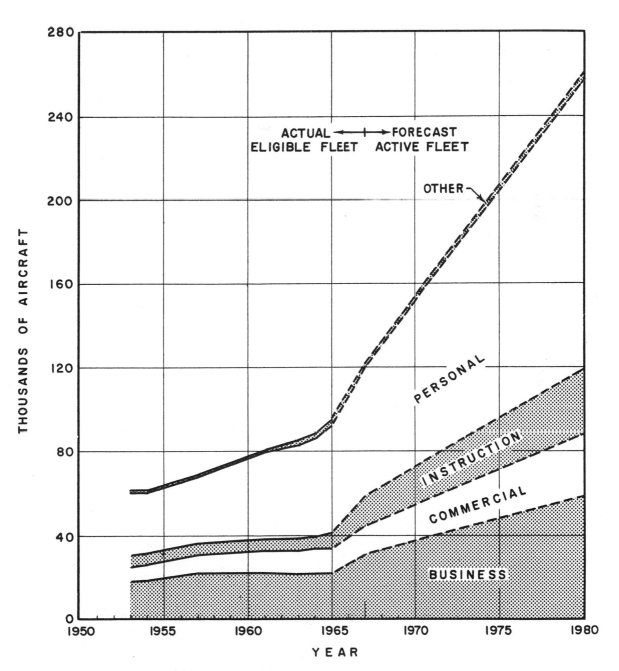

SOURCE: HISTORY - FAA STATISTICAL HANDBOOK
FORECAST - SPEAS ANALYSIS

these flights interacted with those at licensed airports. Weather during this time period was considered to be representative.

The following relevant passenger summary data was extracted and developed from this report:

Airport	General Aviation Itinerant Operations	General Aviation Occupants	Itinerant* Occupants/ Operation
Detroit Airports	210,123	439,788	2.09
All Air Carrier Airports	704,153	1,473,792	2.10
Other Licensed Airports	740,480	1,549,825	2.09
Total	1,444,633	3,023,617	2.09

*SPEAS Calculation Using Data in Columns 2 and 3.

The "occupants" include pilots as well as passengers. This definition is used, since it is all inclusive and accounts for the fact that in small aircraft operations, the distinction between the pilot and end-user (passenger) is irrelevant.

As can be seen from this review, data collected from 137 individual airports showed that an average of 2.1 passengers (counting pilots) were carried on each General Aviation flight. Since 1962, the trend in aircraft size has been to increase — in terms of seats available per aircraft. Consequently, the average number of occupants per aircraft has increased.

b) *FAA 1966 General Aviation Study (1965 Data)*

The FAA in May, 1966, released a Staff Study entitled "General Aviation Occupant Load Fac-

tor", using data obtained during August, 1965. This study reached the following summary conclusions:

• General Aviation Load Factor 53%
• Occupants Per Itinerant Flight 3.1
• Itinerant Passengers
  for CY-1965 .... 39.4 million
• Total (Itinerant and Local) Passengers for CY-1965 would approach that carried by the 77.8 million domestic air carrier enplaned originations.

Other data relevant to this survey is shown in Figures 52 and 53, taken from the FAA, May 1966, Staff Study.

c) *FAA 1968 Air Taxi Study (1966 Data)*

The FAA Study released in May 1968, entitled "1966 Census of Air Taxi Operators", contains useful reference information relating to the volume of passengers and cargo carried by Air Taxi operators during 1966. The relevant values from this study appear in Figures 54-56. The information in Figure 56 may be recapped as follows:

Air Taxi Passengers per Departure 2.17
Air Taxi Pounds Cargo per Departure 162

It is seen that the average passenger per departure value tends to converge on a figure of approximately 2.1 and that there is little significant divergence from this value.

Figure 52
GENERAL AVIATION LOAD FACTOR SURVEY DATA
(As of August 1965)

Type of Aircraft	Number of Seats Available	Number of Seats Occupied	% Load Factor	Average Seats Available	*Occupants/ Departure
Single-Engine Piston					
1-3 Place	50,100	37,145	74%	2.0	1.5
4 Places and Over	485,845	292,183	60%	4.2	2.5
Total	535,945	329,328	61%	3.8	2.3
Multi-Engine Piston	556,870	271,416	49%	9.1	4.5
Turbine	127,264	51,206	40%	18.1	7.2
Total	1,220,079	651,950	53%	5.8	3.1

*Derived value from prior two columns
Source: FAA Staff Study "General Aviation Occupant Load Factor," May, 1966

Figure 53

GENERAL AVIATION LOAD FACTORS
BY TYPE OF AIRCRAFT
(As of August, 1965)

Reciprocating Single Engine

1-3 Place
Flight Plans Filed	24,863
Seats Available	50,100
Seats Occupied	37,145
Load Factor	74%
Occupants/Flight	1.5*

4 Place and Over
Flight Plans Filed	116,144
Seats Available	485,845
Seats Occupied	292,183
Load Factor	60%
Occupants/Flight	2.5*

Multi-Engine Piston

Under 12,500 lbs.
Flight Plans Filed	51,235
Seats Available	320,843
Seats Occupied	178,070
Load Factor	56%
Occupants/Flight	3.5*

Over 12,500 lbs.
Flight Plans Filed	9,627
Seats Available	236,027
Seats Occupied	93,346
Load Factor	40%
Occupants/Flight	9.7*

Turbine

Turboprop
Flight Plans Filed	4,187
Seats Available	89,421
Seats Occupied	30,659
Load Factor	34%
Occupants/Flight	7.3*

Jet
Flight Plans Filed	2,860
Seats Available	37,843
Seats Occupied	20,547
Load Factor	54%
Occupants/Flight	7.2*

*Derived from data in this column

Source: FAA Staff Study, "General Aviation Occupant Load Factor," May, 1966.

Figure 54

1966 CENSUS OF AIR TAXI OPERATORS
ESTIMATE OF TOTALS WITH IMPUTATION

	Estimated Total
Departures	
Non-Scheduled Flights	
Small Non-Scheduled Operators	914,849
Large and Scheduled Operators	852,558
Total Non-Scheduled Departures	1,767,407
Scheduled Flights	378,614
Total, All Departures	2,146,021
Passengers	
Non-Scheduled Flights	
Small Non-Scheduled Operators	1,493,198
Large and Scheduled Operators	1,851,832
Total Non-Scheduled Passengers	3,345,030
Scheduled Flights	1,307,560
Total, All Passengers	4,652,590
Cargo (Tons)	
Non-Scheduled Flights	
Small Non-Scheduled Operators	38,939
Large and Scheduled Operators	15,412
Total Non-Scheduled Cargo	54,351
Scheduled Flights	119,951
Total, All Cargo	174,302

Source: FAA, "1966 Census of Air Taxi Operators," May 1968.

Figure 55

SCHEDULED AND NON-SCHEDULED OPERATORS BY FLEET SIZE GROUP:
AVERAGE HOURS AND PASSENGERS

Number of Aircraft Operated	Operators		Average Hours Flown Per Aircraft[1]		Median Hours Flown per Operator		Average Passengers Per Departure[2]		
	Sched.	Non-Sched.	Sched.	Non-Sched.	Sched.	Non-Sched.	Sched.	Non-Sched.	Total
1	8	663	563	206	563	206	3.3	1.6	1.7
2	18	426	574	194	1148	389	3.8	1.8	2.0
3	16	290	491	215	1473	646	3.7	1.7	2.0
4-10	70	610	545	260	4874	2080	3.5	1.6	2.1
11-21	12	82	567	307	8869	3941	3.1	1.6	1.8
22 & Over	0	11	—	129	—	3535	—	2.1	2.1
	124	2082							

[1] Average hours for 1, 2, and 3 aircraft operators; median of average hours flown using each increment for "4 aircraft and over" groupings.
[2] All flights have been treated as passenger carrying flights.
Note: Average and median hours flown are Air Taxi portion of aircraft utilization; other hours flown not included
Source: FAA, "1966 Census of Air Taxi Operators," May 1968.

Figure 56

ESTIMATED PASSENGERS AND CARGO PER DEPARTURE
(As Prepared from FAA 1966 Census of Air Taxi Operators)

	Passengers/ Departure	Pounds Cargo/ Departure
Non-Scheduled		
Small Non-Scheduled Operators	1.63	85
Large and Scheduled Operators	2.17	36
Total Non-Scheduled Departures	1.89	61
Scheduled Flights	3.45	633
Total	2.17	162

Source: Derived from preceding Figure 54.

3. *Special Surveys Conducted for this Study (June 1968 Data)*

It was considered advisable to supplement the historical studies previously described in order to obtain more current information and supplementary data, particularly on non-Air Taxi operations.

Special field surveys were conducted therefore at LaGuardia, Teterboro, Westchester and Islip (MacArthur) airports for a period of several days to a week at each location during June 1968. In addition, data for Tulsa, for San Jose and for certain Air Taxi operations were also analyzed.

The summarized results of these studies are shown in Figures 57-59. This geographic and operational cross-section is considered to be suitably representative of General Aviation operations to enable the preparation of a satisfactory estimate of the passengers and cargo now being carried by General Aviation aircraft.

The data in the foregoing Figures may be summarized as follows for:

Non-Air Taxi Operations

- Occupants per Operation 2.8
- Load Factor 51%
- Pounds of Cargo per Operation 1.2
- Occupants per Jet Operation 4.1
- Occupants per Turboprop Operation .. 4.5
- Occupants per Reciprocating Operation 2.8

Limited data was collected on Air Taxi operations which indicated that in the New York area an average of 3.5 passengers (no pilots included) were carried per operation.

This survey also developed data of a more detailed nature, as shown in the following Figure, which enabled occupancy and cargo traffic values to be classified by type of aircraft (Jet, Turboprop, and Reciprocating Engine).

4. *Development of Passenger Movements*

a) *Present Passenger Movements*

The SPEAS special survey shows that an average of 2.8 occupants (passengers and pilots) are presently carried on each General Aviation (non-Air Taxi) flight. This value consists of 3.2 for itinerant flights and 1.9 for local flights. The results are considered to be a reliable determination because of the nature of the survey and also because it is confirmed by prior surveys. For example, the FAA 1966 Staff Study showed that 3.1 itinerant occupants were carried per departure; this agrees closely with the SPEAS survey value of 3.2 and indicates the upward trend since the FAA 1965 data. This trend is further supported by the 1962 Michigan State results which showed there were 2.1 itinerant occupants per departure.

Air Taxis carry more occupants per flight. The FAA 1968 Air Taxi Study showed that in 1966 there were an average of 2.2 passengers (excluding pilots) per departure. This, with some amount of escalation, is within the range of the 3.5 occupants (passengers only) value determined in the SPEAS Air Taxi survey. In view of the relatively low percentage of total traffic carried by Air Taxi Operators, it is considered to be compatible for estimating purposes. It is judged, therefore, that the average value of 3.0 total occupants per aircraft for all General Aviation flights is proper for 1967-1968.

Figure 57

AIRCRAFT OCCUPANCY SURVEY SUMMARY, JUNE 1968
(NO AIR TAXI OPERATIONS)

Item	LGA	ISL	TEB	SJO	TUL	HNP	Totals
Total Occupants*	2,227	466	693	401	308	264	4,359
Total Operations	621	225	328	173	83	111	1,541
Total Occupants/Operation	3.6	2.1	2.1	2.3	3.7	2.4	2.8
Load Factor (%)	43%	62%	49%	57%	48%	38%	51%
Itinerant Occupants*	2,136	217	424	166	308	254	3,505
Itinerant Operations	581	83	173	60	83	101	1,081
Occupants/Itinerant Operation	3.7	2.6	2.5	2.8	3.7	2.5	3.2
Load Factor (%)	43%	57%	46%	59%	48%	38%	45%
Local Occupants*	91	249	269	235	—	10	854
Local Operations	40	142	155	113	—	10	460
Occupants/Local Operation	2.3	1.8	1.7	2.1	—	1.0	1.9
Load Factor (%)	58%	67%	55%	56%	—	30%	53%

Note: Survey data collected throughout the day (approximately 7:00 a.m.-7:00 p.m.).
    Not all aircraft operations were recorded each day.
Abbreviations used: LGA — LaGuardia; ISL — Islip; TEB — Teterboro; SJO — San Jose; TUL —
Tulsa; HPN — Westchester.
*Including Pilots
Source: SPEAS Survey and Analysis, June 1968

Figure 58

GENERAL AVIATION
AIRCRAFT CARGO SURVEY SUMMARY, JUNE 1968
(NO AIR TAXI OPERATIONS)

Summary	Total Pounds	Total Operations	Pounds/ Operation
LaGuardia	1,430	621	2.2
Islip	100	225	0.4
Teterboro	0	328	0
Tulsa	0	83	0
San Jose	0	173	0
Westchester	380	111	3.4
Total	1,910	1,541	1.2

Note: Survey data collected throughout the day (approximately 7:00 a.m.-7:00 p.m.)
    Not all operations were recorded each day.
Source: SPEAS Survey and Analysis, June 1968.

Figure 59

GENERAL AVIATION
AIRCRAFT SURVEY, MAY 1968
(AIR TAXI ONLY)

Summary	Passengers	Total Operations	Passengers/ Operation
LaGuardia	883	300	3.0
Newark	1,034	345	3.0
Kennedy	2,037	460	4.4
Total	3,954	1,145	3.5

Note: 1) Survey data obtained for the month of May 1968.
        Note that pilots are not included in the data
Source: SPEAS Analysis

In another section of this report entitled, "Aircraft Movements", it was established that in 1967, there were 98 million General Aviation aircraft movements. Applying the value of 3.0 occupants per aircraft to one-half of this movement figure, it is determined that there now are approximately 150 million nonstop passengers carried per year. If passengers average 1.5 stops per trip, then approximately 100 million passengers are carried per year by General Aviation.

b) *Forecast Passenger Movements*

As previously stated, the present 98 million aircraft movements are projected to expand as follows:

1975 — 168.7 million
1980 — 237.4 million

The average number of occupants per aircraft flight will also increase, as evidenced by the past growth values discussed in the preceding section (a), and as is apparent on the basis of common sense. Past data indicates the following growth rate for itinerant occupants:

Year	Source	Occupants Flight
1962	Michigan State Study	2.1
1965	FAA Staff Study	3.1
1968	SPEAS Survey	3.3

The occupants per flight ratio for the period to 1980 is forecast to increase moderately. It will be limited by the continued heavy preponderance of 1-3 place and 4+ place aircraft in the General Aviation fleet. (Refer to previous aircraft population forecast section of this report). The relative increase in the quantity of larger models of aircraft such as multi-engine reciprocating and turbine types will, however, result in more occupants being carried per aircraft. It is estimated that the present ratio of 3.0 established by the SPEAS analytical results should increase uniformly to a value of approximately 4.0 by 1980. This is equivalent to an

Figure 60

AIRCRAFT OCCUPANCY SURVEY SUMMARY BY AIRCRAFT CATEGORY FOR JUNE 1968
(NO AIR TAXI OPERATIONS)

	Total Occupants	Total Operations	Occupants/ Operation	Load Factor
Jet Aircraft				
LaGuardia	516	127	4.1	38.3%
Tulsa	18	4	4.5	23.6%
Teterboro	20	6	3.3	35.4%
MacArthur	0	0	—	—
Westchester	43	13	3.3	30.1%
San Jose	55	10	5.5	50.1%
Total	652	160	4.7	37.1%
Turboprop Aircraft				
LaGuardia	624	133	4.7	33.1%
Tulsa	64	9	7.1	60.4%
Teterboro	45	13	3.5	39.1%
MacArthur	21	4	5.2	47.3%
Westchester	42	17	2.8	29.2%
San Jose	7	2	3.5	43.1%
Total	803	178	4.5	35.3%
Piston Aircraft				
LaGuardia	1087	361	3.0	55.6%
Tulsa	226	70	3.2	49.9%
Teterboro	628	309	2.1	70.1%
MacArthur	445	221	2.0	63.2%
Westchester	179	81	2.2	43.6%
San Jose	339	161	2.1	59.2%
Total	2904	1203	2.4	58.2%

Source: SPEAS Survey Analysis

average growth rate of 2.4 percent per year, which is close to the rate of 2.3 percent per year experienced between 1965 and 1968 for itinerant aircraft shown in the preceding tabulation.

This average rate of 4.0 by 1980 is considered to account also for Air Taxi passengers only, and represents almost a doubling by 1980 of the FAA 1966 value of 2.2 passengers.

By applying the foregoing derivation to the projected movement values, the following forecast of passengers carried on General Aviation aircraft is obtained:

Year	Movements (Millions)	Occupants/ Flight	Approximate* Passengers Carried (Millions/ Year)
1967	98	3.0	150
1975	169	3.6	300
1980	237	4.0	475

*Non-stop Movements

5. Development of Cargo Volumes

There are no known earlier studies of cargo volumes carried by General Aviation for other than Air Taxi operators, which are reliable.

The volume of cargo carried by non-Air Taxi operators is known to be very low. The SPEAS survey was directed in part towards attempting to quantify this value. The results showed that on an overall average basis, only 1.2 pounds are carried per flight. A special large-scale study extending over a long time period (such as 12 months) could establish a more refined value, but the 1.2 figure is based on a representative sample of six airports.

In 1967, there were 98 million General Aviation movements, or 49 million departures, of which approximately 95 percent were non-Air Taxi (Refer to FAA 1966 Census of Air Taxi Operators, which showed 2.15 million Air Taxi departures in 1966). Using a value of 1.2 pounds per departure, the cargo carried by non-Air Taxi operations would total approximately 60 million pounds (.95 x 49 million x 1.2). This compares with the 1966 Air Taxi volume (Refer to FAA 1966 report) of approximately 350 million pounds, or a General Avia-

tion total of 410 million. This is a very nominal value. Emergency, random and specialized services, such as those accomplished by corporations, would add a significant and varying increment to this total. It would appear, that 500 million pounds a year may be carried by General Aviation as of 1967. Also, Air Taxi operations are now being established which are heavily cargo oriented — up to 100%.

During the coming years, the growth in Air Carrier cargo will have a pronounced impact on Air Taxi cargo operations. Air Carrier cargo is estimated to grow at an annual rate of 15-20 percent for the 1970-1980 time period. Air Taxi operations will participate in this Air Carrier growth rate, but to a lesser extent. From evaluations of both of these potentials, it is SPEAS's forecast that Air Taxi cargo can be expected to achieve an average annual compound growth rate of 12 percent during the 13-year period 1967-1980.

Based upon the FAA report of 174,302 tons (350 million pounds) carried in 1966, the 1980 cargo volume would be 4.9 times larger, or approximately .85 million tons, or 1,700 million pounds. The volume contributed by non-Air Taxi would be a relatively small percentage of this value, depending upon growth in total movements and volume carried per movement, and is estimated to be approximately 200 million pounds, based upon survey data. The total General Aviation cargo projected to be carried in 1980 is, therefore, approximately 1.0 million tons.

An important element of this General Aviation cargo will be airmail, but the lack of quantitative historical data precludes an individual forecast.

Summary

The principal conclusions of the analysis as developed and discussed above, are as follows:

Passengers carried, 1967 .... 150 million
Passengers carried, 1980 .... 457 million
Cargo carried, 1967 .... 250,000 tons
Cargo carried, 1980 .... 1,000,000 tons

N.B. A passenger in this context represents one flight by one passenger and includes pilots.

CHAPTER EIGHT

ECONOMIC IMPACT

General

In analyzing the impact of General Aviation on the economy, the approach is based upon two areas of inquiry. The most important portion of the analysis is concerned with a detailed specification of the contributions of the General Aviation industry and related industrial sectors to the Gross National Product.

The approach employed in this study results in the estimation of the gross contribution of General Aviation to the economy. It evaluates the direct gross contribution of those economic sectors immediately involved in General Aviation. This approach also examines the indirect impacts which result from the manufacture of intermediate products and investment goods that provide the necessary inputs to these sectors. In essence, therefore, this study evaluates the total impact on the economy of all activity resulting both directly and indirectly from the existence of General Aviation. Another way of viewing this methodology is to consider the question of what would be the total effect on the economy of a sudden and complete cessation of all General Aviation activities. If it were assumed that there was no substitution of other transportation modes for the services performed by General Aviation, the total economic value associated with such a curtailment of activity would be inclusive of both the direct and indirect impacts mentioned above. For example, not only does such an approach consider the direct economic loss associated with the cessation of aircraft production, but in addition assumes that the investment (machinery and equipment) required to produce the aircraft would not have been made.

It is clear, however, that an assumption of zero substitutability between General Aviation and other transportation modes is very unrealistic. In light of this, a consideration of the actual economic value of General Aviation to the U. S. economy should reflect the savings from using General Aviation in the performance of its service vis-a-vis the costs which would be incurred if it were necessary to perform the identical function by the alternative modes.[1]

This approach to the problem assumes that sufficient time elapses in order to permit the complete adjustment to the alternative transportation modes. The adjustment includes the suppliers of all intermediate products and producers of the investment goods formerly employed in the General Aviation industry. To continue with the example cited above, when substitution effects are taken into account, it is assumed that the value of investment (machinery and equipment) used to produce the aircraft is now employed in its next most productive use. There can be no question that this approach measures, most precisely, the true economic impact of the General Aviation industry.

Given the purpose of this research which is to determine the aggregate impact of General Aviation on the U. S. economy, however, it is felt that such an approach does not most adequately reveal the nature of the impact which

---

[1] To estimate the benefits of performing comparable services by General Aviation in terms of each alternative mode of transportation would require an additional research project which would deal solely with this problem. Employing a matrix of U. S. industrial classifications, it would be possible to separate General Aviation from the more general classification of which it is a component. Computation of the values of the matrix prior to and following the removal of the vector of coefficients for General Aviation, and calculation of the difference of these two values would yield not only the value of the General Aviation industry to the economy, but also the interrelationship of General Aviation with all the remaining industrial classifications given by the matrix. In a similar fashion the loss in GNP from performing the services of General Aviation by other modes could be estimated by adjusting the relevant industrial classification to be taken into account the provision of the service formerly performed by the General Aviation industry.

GAMA seeks to ascertain. As a result, the approach of this study will be to concentrate on the gross contribution to economic activity resulting from the existence of General Aviation and related activities.

In measuring productive economic activity, the GNP accounts attempt to measure the flow of final goods and services resulting from all productive activity within a given year. The aggregation of all expenditures is classified into four areas: consumption, investment, government spending and the balance of trade (exports-imports). In symbols: GNP = C+I+G+ (X-M). If the economy is studied on an aggregate basis, the value of goods and services are placed in that category which reflects their final usage. This same categorization is employed when analyzing the deposition of the final output of any specific industry. For example, when analyzing the output of the General Aviation aircraft industry under this methodology, the concern is with the use made of the aircraft produced. Were they sold for pleasure flying (an example of consumption)? Were they used by a corporation for executive travel (investment)? Were they purchased by the government? Were they sold to foreign users and thus enter into the balance of trade? It is important to note that this classification is used to allocate the final usage of the output of a given industrial sector. Thus in talking about the investment component of GNP, attributable to the General Aviation aircraft industry, reference is to the aircraft which became the intermediate products of another industry. In the example cited above the airplane purchased by a corporation becomes an investment good in the production of their final output. In terms of the terminology to be employed in this study, this aircraft sale has a direct impact on GNP when viewed from the point of view of General Aviation, and an indirect impact vis-a-vis the corporation. Carrying the argument one step further, it is important to emphasize that the investment which goes into the production of aircraft, or the investment in plant and equipment of fixed base operators, for example, is considered to have an indirect impact on GNP given the orientation of this study. (The direct impact of

this plant and equipment expenditures is attributable to the capital goods producers themselves). This detailed discussion, although somewhat laborious, will serve to clarify the details of the analysis set forth below.

The total gross value of production of General Aviation aircraft is first considered with specific attention being paid to delineating production for domestic consumption and production for exports. Other direct impacts which are considered include: the value of avionics installed in used aircraft, the transactions costs associated with the sale of used aircraft, and an analysis of the user costs associated with the operation of aircraft.

The analysis of the indirect impact provided by the existence of the General Aviation industry will consider the investment which is made in all related activity. Specifically this will include the investment of the producers of aircraft, the fixed investment mode in the distribution facilities of the industry, and the capital expenditures of fixed base operators. The other major category under the heading of indirect impacts relates to the level of government expenditures on General Aviation, including expenditures by the states and municipalities as well as by the Federal Government.

1. *Gross Contribution of General Aviation to the Economy*

a) *Value of Production and Final Sales*

In reviewing the value of production of all General Aviation aircraft, the gross output of the industry is considered. This approach has two distinct advantages. First of all, it is not necessary to become involved in a separation of the value added by the production process as distinct from the value of the intermediate goods needed in the production of the final output[2]. Secondly, it is not necessary to specify the particular usages in which the total production of the aircraft are employed. However, for purposes of analyzing in detail the balance of trade

---

[2]Technically, however, some information is lost through this approach since the value added is considered as a direct impact of GA on GNP, whereas, the production and value of the intermediate goods should be considered as having an indirect impact.

impact of General Aviation the value of aircraft exported is separated from the total value of production. The residual of these two — the production of aircraft for domestic consumption — is the series upon which the projection of the fleet is based.

One remaining point should be clarified before turning to an analysis of existing data. If an industrial sector is analyzed through the $C+I+G+(X-M)$ approach, it should be noted that the net balance of trade is the relevant parameter. This is the case because the value of imports (M) are already contained in $C+I+G$ (the particular allocation depends upon their use). Since the GNP accounts reflect only the value of productive activity taking place within the U. S. it is necessary to deduct the value of imports which are included in $C+I+G$. When the contribution of an industry is considered from the point of view of value of production, however, it is not necessary to net out the value of imports since our production figures include only the value of domestic production, regardless of whether it is sold abroad or at home. Therefore, in this approach the relevant trade parameter becomes gross exports.

The history of the value of production of General Aviation aircraft are from the FAA.[3] This series gives the value of shipments of such fixed wing aircraft in FOB prices. These prices do not include any mark-up, sales tax, or distribution cost. There is a general rule of thumb within the industry that the stated retail price involves mark-up of approximately 33 percent over the value of the completed units at the factory. The effective selling price, however, is considered to be 95 percent of this figure. Thus to adjust the manufacturer's price, in order to attain the effective selling price, the former is multiplied by 1.26 (1.26 = 1.33 × .95). Figure 6 shows the value of shipments of fixed wing General Aviation aircraft from 1956-66, prior to and following the price adjustment. In 1966 the FOB value was $471,720,000 and the estimated sales value was $594,367,000.

An additional source of information is available from the production value collected by selected AIA manufacturers.[4] These production figures are given in terms of the net billing price paid to the manufacturer and are also shown in

[3]Federal Aviation Agency, FAA Statistical Handbook of Aviation 1966 Edition, page 100.

[4]Aerospace News, AIA

Figure 61

SHIPMENTS OF FIXED WING AIRCRAFT MANUFACTURED IN THE UNITED STATES OF AMERICA (THOUSANDS OF DOLLARS)

Year	Shipments of Fixed Wing Aircraft F.O.B. Prices*	Effective* Retail Value: 26% Mark-Up	Net Manufacturing Billing Price**	Effective Retail Value: 26% Mark-Up	Column 4 ÷ Column 2
1956	$104,952	$132,240	$103,791	$130,777	$98.89
1957	100,441	126,556	99,652	125,562	99.21
1958	102,141	128,698	101,939	128,443	99.80
1959	147,585	185,957	129,876	163,644	88.00
1960	177,213	223,288	151,220	190,537	85.33
1961	151,302	190,641	124,323	156,647	82.16
1962	156,816	197,588	136,837	172,415	87.25
1963	174,201	219,493	153,415	193,303	88.06
1964	236,859	298,442	198,876	250,583	83.96
1965	379,772	478,513	318,266	401,015	83.80
1966	471,720	594,367	444,910	560,587	94.31

*Source: FAA Statistical Handbook of Aviation
**Source: AIA

Column 3 of Figure 61 along with the estimated effective retail values (which once again, are based on the method described above) shown in Column 4. The last column of Figure 61 shows the percentages of the total value of total shipments which are produced by the selected AIA manufacturers. This comparison of the two sources of data is presented because the AIA data is the source of the detailed estimation of the production function of General Aviation aircraft.

The analysis of the value of production to this point has been concerned solely with fixed wing aircraft. In order to get the total value of production it is necessary to consider in addition the value of all rotorcraft shipments.[5] Figure 62 gives these figures for 1958-66 and the corresponding estimate of the effective selling price. Column 3 of Figure 62 gives the total value of production. The total estimate for 1966 is $631,339,000. Once having obtained the total value of production it is of interest to determine the relative breakdown between exports and domestic consumption. Export figures since 1965 have been collected on a basis different from that used in previous years and this new data is not comparable with the previous figures. As far as can be determined, until 1965 total General Aviation export figures included

[5]FAA Handbook, Ibid., page 111

only aircraft with airframe weight under 3,000 pounds, whereas, since 1965 export data includes all aircraft. However, export figures are available for the value of light transports and General Aviation aircraft under 20,000 pounds airframe weight by selected U. S. manufacturers from 1960-1967.[6] The value of these exports was 86.5 percent and 84.6 percent of the total exports of General Aviation aircraft in 1965 and 1966 respectively. Assuming that the value of exports by the selected manufacturers averaged 85 percent of total exports over the period back to 1960, the total export of fixed-wing aircraft from 1960 through 1964 can be estimated by dividing the data given for selected manufacturers by this percentage. The results of this calculation are shown in Column 2 of Figure 63. Given the value of fixed-wing aircraft exported, the total value of exports can be attained by adding the value of exported rotary wing aircraft.[7] The value of rotary wing aircraft exports and total General Aviation exports are shown in Columns 3 and 4 of Figure 63. Column 5 of that Figure shows the annual portion of total output exported over the seven-year period for which data is available.[8] This shows that during the seven-year period ex-

[6]AIA, Aerospace Facts and Figures 1967, page 78.
[7]Aerospace Facts and Figures, page 81.
[8]It should be pointed out that these percentages reflect approximate values, since it is not clear as to the exact prices at which these exports were valued.

Figure 62

SHIPMENTS OF ROTORCRAFT AND TOTAL VALUE OF ALL GENERAL AVIATION AIRCRAFT MANUFACTURED IN THE UNITED STATES OF AMERICA (THOUSANDS OF DOLLARS)

Year	F.O.B. Prices*	Retail Value 26% Mark-Up*	Total Production of General Aviation in Effective Retail Prices**
1958	$26,212	$33,027	$161,725
1959	24,525	30,902	216,859
1960	16,064	20,241	243,529
1961	15,890	20,021	210,662
1962	27,171	34,235	231,824
1963	42,263	53,251	272,744
1964	44,078	55,538	353,980
1965	49,918	62,897	541,409
1966	29,243	36,972	631,339

*Source: FAA Statistical Handbook of Aviation
**Column 2+ Column 2 of Figure 61.

Figure 63

SELECTED DATA ON EXPORTS OF GENERAL AVIATION AIRCRAFT
(THOUSANDS OF DOLLARS)

Year	Fixed Wing Exports by Selected AIA Members	Total Fixed Wing Exports	Rotary Wing Exports Non-Military	Total General Aviation Exports Non-Military	Exports as % of Total Production at Factory Value
1960	$27,313	$32,131	$ 7,700	$ 39,831	20.6
1961	29,790	35,047	6,800	41,847	25.0
1962	30,939	36,397	8,800	45,197	24.6
1963	35,061	41,247	9,800	51,047	23.6
1964	44,118	51,903	14,600	66,503	23.7
1965	59,596	68,900	16,200	85,100	19.8
1966	75,373	89,100	11,600	100,700	20.1

Source: FAA Statistical Handbook of Aviation.

amined, exports accounted for from 20-25 percent of total production of General Aviation aircraft at factory values.

The value of production of aircraft for domestic use as a component of GNP has been constructed by category of aircraft. Production rates by category for 1967 were estimated from an extension of GAMA data to the total industry, and projections for 1975 and 1980 were evolved from considerations of additions to fleet and attrition rates by category as discussed above.

Unit prices were determined from analysis of weighted averages of costs to the user. A major element of this analysis was GAMA factory shipments and billing data. Factory billings were increased by 26 percent to arrive at cost to the user, with this markup reflecting the typical 33 percent margin on cost allowed in aircraft list prices less 5 percent negotiated discount.

The value and units of production of General Aviation aircraft manufactured for domestic use for the years 1967, 1975 and 1980 are shown in Figure 64. This figure indicates the 99 percent growth forecast in unit production from 1967 to 1980 accompanied by a 249 percent increase in total dollar value, with these values stated in constant dollars.

The overall average unit price reflected by these numbers increases from $43.8 million

in 1967 to $77.0 million in 1980. The great majority of this increase stems from the change in mix forecast to occur during this period. The unit prices by category, which are shown in Figure 65 reflect modest increases in the largest volume categories and decreases in those categories for which a change in the mix within the category has been forecast.

The increase for those categories with no mix change is calculated at a compound growth rate of 1.2 percent per year, which is based on an analysis of industry experience in recent years, weighted to delete the effect of mix changes. From 1954 to 1964 the industry as a whole experienced a 2.4 percent annual growth in unit sales value in constant dollars. Further analysis indicated that the use of a 1.2 percent rate removes the majority of the impact of the introduction of larger aircraft during this period, which was required since mix changes are factored into the forecast through the category breakdowns.

In the large turboprop category it has been assumed that all production in 1975 and 1980 will be of a type smaller and less expensive than the Gulfstream I, which was the basis for the 1967 unit values. It is also forecast that in the turbojet category there will be a new generation of smaller aircraft introduced in the 1970s, and that this smaller type will account for 20 percent of domestic sales in 1975 and 40 percent in 1980. Similarly in rotorcraft, it is as-

Figure 64

GENERAL AVIATION AIRCRAFT PRODUCTION FOR DOMESTIC CONSUMPTION
UNITS AND VALUE OF CONSUMER EXPENDITURES FOR NEW AIRCRAFT

Aircraft Category	1967 Units	1967 Dollars (000)	1975 Units	1975 Dollars (000)	1980 Units	1980 Dollars (000)
Single Engine 1-3 Place	3,912	41,100	3,040	35,000	3,270	39,900
Single Engine 4+ Place	5,078	116,800	11,100	280,800	12,700	340,400
Multi-Engine to 12,500 lbs. to 600 HP	955	67,000	1,630	125,800	1,760	144,200
Multi-Engine to 12,500 lbs. Over 600 HP	351	52,600	580	95,700	620	108,500
Multi-Engine Turboprop to 12,500 lbs.	149	65,500	340	164,400	560	287,300
Multi-Engine Turboprop Over 12,500 lbs.	7	10,200	90	59,400	160	112,000
Multi-Engine Turbojet	88	99,400	250	278,700	450	471,300
Rotorcraft	250	22,500	790	68,400	1,990	156,800
Unspecified	60	200	80	300	50	200
Total	10,850	475,300	17,900	1,108,500	21,560	1,660,600

Note: Values are stated in constant 1967 dollars.
Source: SPEAS Analysis.

Figure 65

AVERAGE UNIT PRICES TO THE USER
GENERAL AVIATION AIRCRAFT BY AIRCRAFT CATEGORY

Thousands of Dollars

Aircraft Category	1967	1975	1980
Single Engine 1-3 Place	$ 10.5	$ 11.5	$ 12.2
Single Engine 4+ Place	23.0	25.3	26.8
Multi-Engine to 12,500 lbs. to 600 HP	70.2	77.2	81.9
Multi-Engine to 12,500 lbs. Over 600 HP	150.0	165.0	175.0
Multi-Engine Turboprop to 12,500 lbs.	439.6	483.5	513.0
Multi-Engine Turboprop Over 12,500 lbs.	1450.0	660.0	700.2
Multi-Engine Turbojet	1129.2	1114.7	1047.4
Rotorcraft	90.0	86.6	78.8
Unspecified	3.0	3.3	3.5

Source: SPEAS Analysis.

Figure 64a

GENERAL AVIATION AIRCRAFT PRODUCTION
FOR DOMESTIC CONSUMPTION
VALUE OF CONSUMER EXPENDITURES (GRAPH)

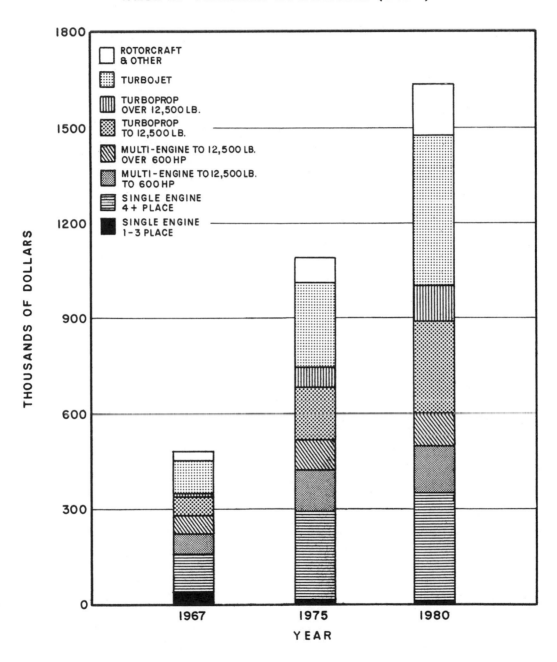

SOURCE: SPEAS ANALYSIS

sumed that new generation, smaller units will account for 25 percent and 50 percent of sales in 1975 and 1980 respectively.

Excluded from these production values are considerations for imports and transfers to the General Aviation fleet from air carriers. Both of these are included in net additions to the active fleet, and thus had to be deleted to arrive at domestic production. Air carrier transfers and imports are each forecast to constitute 20 percent of the net additions of large turbo-props. Imports are further forecast to make up 20 percent of the small turboprops, 30 percent of the turbojets and 10 percent of the rotorcraft.

The value of production of aircraft for export is forecast to go from $76,500,000 in 1967 to $173,700,000 in 1975 and $253,600,000 in 1980. The estimate of the value of exports is based on the projection of export units. To this was applied an estimated unit price which is related to the projected unit value of domestic sales. The historical relationship between domestic and export average unit prices has been a declining one. It is estimated that this relationship will continue to decline at about 1 percent per year. This reflects the changing composition of the export market relative to domestic sales, whereby the upgrading of export types is not expected to keep up with that forecast for domestic sales.

It is estimated that exports of General Aviation engines and avionics amounted to $70,-000,000 in 1967 and that these exports will grow at the same rate as that of the value of exports of aircraft. This indicates values of $159,000,000 in 1975 and $232,000,000 in 1980 for these exports.

b) *Production and Value of Avionics*

The value of all instrumentation installed in General Aviation aircraft has been growing rapidly in recent years and in 1967 reached a total value of more than $142,000,000. A major portion of this total, however, is installed in new aircraft and its value and contribution to GNP have already been considered in the estimates for the value of production. As a result it is necessary to isolate the value of total avionic equipment installed in used aircraft, in order to avoid double counting. Data showing the desired breakdown has been prepared by the Aircraft Electronics Association. Their estimation of the values of avionics for 1966 and 1967 are as follows:[9]

	1966	1967
Installed in new aircraft	$107,126,000	$ 96,421,000
Equipment for retro-fit	25,000,000	26,000,000
Installation and service (includes parts and labor)	21,000,000	19,747,000
	$153,126,000	$142,168,000

Assuming that the installation and service charges are primarily associated with the re-fitting of older aircraft with new avionics equipment, the sum of the last two items listed can be attributed as the total value associated with the installation of avionics in used aircraft. The resulting figure of $45,747,000 is thus the estimation of the contribution of avionics to economic activity, over and above that already included under the value of production.

It is forecast that this value will grow at the same rate as the total value of domestic sales of new aircraft to $106,700,000 in 1975 and $159,800,000 in 1980. This is considered to be a conservative estimate since, with the upgrading which is forecast to occur in sophistication of aircraft and equipment, the rate of growth in the average value of installed avionics in General Aviation aircraft will be even greater.

c) *Transaction Costs of the Used Aircraft Market*

To this point, concentration has been on the contribution of General Aviation to GNP associated with new production of aircraft and avionics equipment. However, there is in addition to the sale of new aircraft an even larger market dealing with the exchange of used aircraft. In GNP accounting the purchase of a used aircraft is treated as a transfer payment, since it reflects no new productive activity. However, the service performed by the dealers or others who act as "middle-men" in these transactions does reflect economic activity over

[9]National Business Aircraft Association, Inc., *Business Flying, Historical Statistical Operational Information,* Special Report 68-8, April 1968; pg. 42.

and above the value of the used aircraft and, therefore, should be included in GNP.

The estimation of the value of this service is derived in the following manner. It is commonly held by the industry that the number of used aircraft transactions is twice the number of new aircraft sales. Taking the total number of aircraft sold in 1967 as approximately 11,000, it can be estimated that the number of used aircraft sales were 22,000. If the average price of used aircraft is considered to be $10,000, it can be stated that the total sales of used aircraft were of the magnitude of $220,-000,000. Making the additional assumption that the total transactions costs are 10 percent of the selling price of used aircraft, the value of the service performed can be estimated at approximately $22,000,000. This figure reflects the net contribution to GNP which is attributable to used General Aviation aircraft sales.

The assumptions regarding the average price of a used aircraft and the dealer mark-up of 10 percent are conservative estimates. It is considered that in cases such as this in which it becomes necessary to make critical assumptions, it is more in the interest of GAMA to insure the validity of the final estimate by not making assumptions which are not clearly warranted from available sources of information.

In projecting this function to 1980, it has been assumed that the average used aircraft price will rise roughly in proportion to the increase in the average new aircraft price, to $15,000 in 1975 and $20,000 in 1980. It is assumed that used transactions will remain twice new sales, and that the dealer mark-up would also continue at 10 percent. These conditions indicate a contribution to GNP of $54,000,000 in 1975 and $86,000,000 in 1980 from the sales of used General Aviation aircraft.

d) *User Cost of Aircraft Operation*

The contribution to GNP of the direct cost of operating General Aviation aircraft is determined by examining the individual ingredients:
- fuel consumption
- oil consumption
- maintenance and overhaul labor
- maintenance and overhaul parts
- insurance
- storage
- landing fees
- charts and publications
- miscellaneous

These individual ingredients were calculated for nine different categories of aircraft used in General Aviation operations.

The costs per hour for 1967 were analyzed on the basis of prior work effort for individual aircraft types. In arriving at the values shown, specific data was factored in order that the total would reflect the weighted average cost for the fleet mixes of the several aircraft types.

The directly variable costs were calculated on a per hour basis, and the fixed annual costs, mainly insurance and storage, were formulated on an annual basis and divided by the appropriate utilization value as discussed in a separate section of this study.

The contribution to GNP attributed to the direct cost of operation of General Aviation aircraft is forecast to increase in constant 1967 dollars from $683.1 million in 1967 to $1,491.0 million in 1975 and to $2,488.0 million in 1980.

An analysis of these amounts by aircraft category is shown in Figure 66. The development of the totals by year is presented in Figures 67, 68 and 69, which show by category the number of aircraft, average utilization and cost per hour flown. Figure 70 presents a comparison of the costs per hour as developed for each of the aircraft categories for the years 1967, 1975 and 1980.

The projections of 1975 and 1980 hourly costs were accomplished in constant 1967 dollars. They basically assume that fuel and oil and fixed cost requirements will not change and that maintenance will increase with the growth in technological sophistication which was discussed above under production values. Another variable, which generally tended to reduce future costs, was the consideration of utilization.

Figure 66

GENERAL AVIATION USER COSTS
1967 — 1975 — 1980
Millions of Dollars

Aircraft Category	1967	1975	1980
Single Engine 1-3 Place	$101.4	$145.3	$159.2
Single Engine 4+ Place	180.3	311.5	492.6
Multi-Engine to 12,500 lbs. to 600 HP	112.9	229.3	321.1
Multi-Engine to 12,500 lbs. Over 600 HP	50.7	121.3	189.5
Multi-Engine Over 12,500 lbs.	41.7	33.5	20.0
Multi-Engine Turboprop to 12,500 lbs.	17.9	108.4	239.3
Multi-Engine Turboprop Over 12,500 lbs.	44.2	112.5	203.5
Multi-Engine Turbojet	91.2	326.9	646.1
Rotorcraft	42.2	101.3	215.6
Unspecified	0.6	1.0	1.1
Total	683.1	1491.0	2488.0

Source: SPEAS Analysis

Figure 67

DEVELOPMENT OF 1967 GENERAL AVIATION USER COSTS

Aircraft Category	Aircraft	Utilization	$/Hour	$ Millions
Single Engine 1-3 Place	41,760	204	11.90	101.4
Single Engine 4+ Place	61,319	174	16.90	180.3
Multi-Engine to 12,500 lbs. to 600 HP	10,423	235	46.10	112.9
Multi-Engine to 12,500 lbs. Over 600 HP	2,864	311	56.90	50.7
Multi-Engine Over 12,500 lbs.	1,222	341	100.00	41.7
Multi-Engine Turboprop to 12,500 lbs.	475	462	81.60	17.9
Multi-Engine Turboprop Over 12,500 lbs.	323	622	220.00	44.2
Multi-Engine Turbojet	787	414	280.00	91.2
Rotorcraft	1,875	346	65.00	42.2
Unspecified	1,152	91	6.00	0.6
Total/Average	122,200	198	27.90	683.1

Source: SPEAS Analysis

Figure 68

DEVELOPMENT OF 1975 GENERAL AVIATION USER COSTS

Aircraft Category	Aircraft	Utilization	$/Hour	$ Millions
Single Engine 1-3 Place	55,400	230 hr.	11.40	145.3
Single Engine 4+ Place	98,200	190	16.70	311.5
Multi-Engine to 12,500 lbs. to 600 HP	19,500	245	48.00	229.3
Multi-Engine to 12,500 lbs. Over 600 HP	6,200	330	59.30	121.3
Multi-Engine Over 12,500 lbs.	800	310	135.00	33.5
Multi-Engine Turboprop to 12,500 lbs.	2,400	550	82.10	108.4
Multi-Engine Turboprop Over 12,500 lbs.	1,000	625	180.00	112.5
Multi-Engine Turbojet	2,600	435	289.00	326.9
Rotorcraft	4,200	349	69.10	101.3
Unspecified	1,700	97	6.00	1.0
Total/Average	192,000	223	34.53	1491.0

Source: SPEAS Analysis

Figure 69

DEVELOPMENT OF 1980 GENERAL AVIATION USER COSTS

Aircraft Category	Aircraft	Utilization	$/Hour	$ Millions
Single Engine 1-3 Place	58,700	240 hr.	11.30	159.2
Single Engine 4+ Place	143,900	210	16.30	492.6
Multi-Engine to 12,500 lbs. to 600 HP	26,000	250	49.40	321.1
Multi-Engine to 12,500 lbs. Over 600 HP	8,700	360	60.50	189.5
Multi-Engine Over 12,500 lbs.	500	250	160.00	20.0
Multi-Engine Turboprop to 12,500 lbs.	4,800	600	83.10	239.3
Multi-Engine Turboprop Over 12,500 lbs.	1,900	630	170.00	203.5
Multi-Engine Turbojet	4,900	450	293.00	646.1
Rotorcraft	8,700	350	70.80	215.6
Unspecified	1,900	100	6.00	1.1
Total/Average	260,000	244	39.13	2488.0

Source: SPEAS Analysis

Figure 69a

GENERAL AVIATION USER COSTS

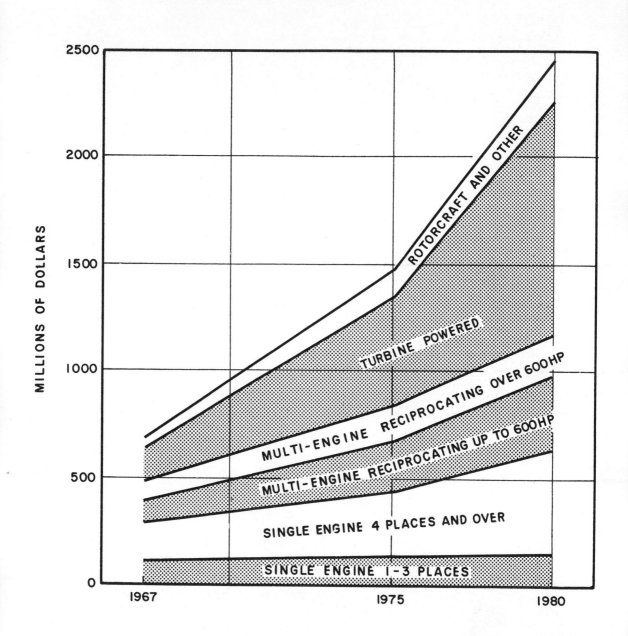

SOURCE: SPEAS ANALYSIS

Figure 70

GENERAL AVIATION AIRCRAFT USER COSTS
1967 — 1975 — 1980
DOLLARS PER HOUR

Aircraft Category	1967	1975	1980
Single Engine 1-3 Place	$ 11.90	$ 11.40	$ 11.30
Single Engine 4+ Place	16.90	16.70	16.30
Multi-Engine to 12,500 lbs. to 600 HP	46.10	48.00	49.40
Multi-Engine to 12,500 lbs. Over 600 HP	56.90	59.30	60.50
Multi-Engine Over 12,500 lbs.	100.00	135.00	160.00
Multi-Engine Turboprop to 12,500 lbs.	81.60	82.10	83.10
Multi-Engine Turboprop Over 12,500 lbs.	220.00	180.00	170.00
Multi-Engine Turbojet	280.00	289.00	293.00
Rotorcraft	65.00	69.10	70.80
Unspecified	6.00	6.00	6.00

Source: SPEAS Analysis.

Changes in utilization alter the base over which fixed annual costs are prorated, and since utilization has been projected generally to increase, the hourly charge for annual expenses generally decreased. The one notable exception was the category of reciprocating multi-engine aircraft over 12,500 lbs. No new production of this type is anticipated, and it is projected that costs will climb and utilization will diminish as the fleet shrinks from the 1,222 in 1967 to the 500 forecast for 1980.

Exceptions to this basic extrapolation of 1967 costs were made in the cases of the large turbo-props, turbojets and rotorcraft where substantial changes in the mix of aircraft within the categories have been projected.

In 1967 the large turboprops consisted of Gulfstream Is, executive F-27s and turboprop Convairs plus a number of retired airline aircraft. The projection of relatively large quantities of smaller aircraft entering this category of the General Aviation fleet and the produc-

tion of current models phasing out, results in the indicated reduction projected in average hourly operating costs. It is forecast that by 1980 two-thirds of the hours flown will be in the smaller group of aircraft within this category.

Similarly, in the turbojet category it is forecast that a new generation of smaller aircraft will be introduced and will account for 15 percent of the operations by 1980, materially dampening the normal growth in hourly costs. In rotorcraft it is projected that a smaller generation of aircraft will account for 20 percent of the hours flown by 1980.

The indicated growth in the average cost per hour for all General Aviation flying from $27.90 in 1967 to $34.53 in 1975 and $39.13 in 1980 is primarily the result of the upgrading in the fleet mix; active single engine aircraft, while increasing by 96.5 percent from 103,079 to 202,600 in 1980, decrease as a percentage of the total fleet from 84.4 percent to 77.9 percent. The more costly multi-engine aircraft and rotorcraft, all of which are relatively more expensive to operate, register strong growth, both absolutely and as percents of the total fleet.

It is principally this upgrading between categories, with a small increment due to the increase within types, which causes total user costs to increase by 264 percent from 1967 to 1980 while hours increase by 160 percent and active aircraft by 113 percent. By way of contrast, GNP is forecast to increase by 73 percent in constant dollar terms in this same thirteen year period.

e) *Pilot Wages and Administrative Overhead*

To estimate pilot wages, hours flown were analyzed by type of flying and then converted to numbers of professional pilots through the application of an assumed utilization. This number of pilots was converted to wages by use of an assumed annual income, which was stated at a level which includes an administrative overhead.

For the purposes of this section it is assumed that one-half of Business and Instruction flying and all of Commercial and Other flying are accomplished by professional pilots. This indicates a total of 11.7 million professional pilot hours in 1967 and 31.4 million hours in 1980. Interpolation places the 1975 value at 23.8 million hours. No specific consideration is made of situations with more than one flight crew member; these circumstances are believed to be reasonably covered by the overall assumptions.

It is assumed that the average person fully employed as a professional General Aviation pilot flew 350 hours per year in 1967, and that this value will increase with the overall increase in utilization to 395 hours in 1975 and 430 hours in 1980. This implies equivalent totals of 33,400, 60,300 and 73,000 full-time professional General Aviation pilots in 1967, 1975 and 1980 respectively. These values are low in comparison to numbers cited in other sources, but it must be remembered that these represent equivalent full-time pilots. There are in fact fewer actual full-time pilots and many more part-time pilots, but for the mechanics of the

methodology it was necessary to impute the equivalent full-time numbers.

Applying to these numbers the value of $15,600 per pilot per year produces total contribution to GNP of $521,000,000 in 1967, $941,000,000 in 1975 and $1,139,000,000 in 1980. The $15,600 includes $12,000 direct salary and 30 percent administrative overhead and profit. This burden allocation covers those general and administrative aspects of commercial operators and corporate aviation departments not picked up through user charges.

f) *Investment*

To this point the direct impact of General Aviation associated with the purchase and use of aircraft has been considered. The investment made in General Aviation is technically viewed as having an indirect impact and can be considered under three major categories.

Investment by Producers

Analysis of aircraft producers is based on data for four companies: Beech, Cessna, Piper and Lear Jet. The sample makes up a substantial proportion of total industry output, its share being 75 percent when expressed in value terms and over 90 percent of the volume during 1967. The production figures for the first three companies listed came from their 1967 annual reports. The Lear Jet data were from their 1966 report which was their last report issued as an independent corporation. It is felt that a company producing only jet aircraft should be included in the sample since it is clear that the production function for jets is not the same as for piston aircraft.

From the information given in these annual reports, it is possible to obtain the net value of property, plant and equipment for the firms for 1966 and 1967, with the 1967 figure for Lear Jet being estimated. By cumulating the capital asset data in the four reports, it is found that the net capital assets on September 30, 1967 were $60,565,816 and on the corresponding date for 1966, $51,067,194. To obtain the investment which took place during the fiscal year (from September 30, 1966 to September 30, 1967) it is only necessary to find the difference of these two numbers. The estimation of the value of investment by the sample during the fiscal year is $9,500,000. This estimate is considered to hold for the calendar year 1967.

The output-investment ratio measured in value terms is considered the same for the remainder of the General Aviation aircraft producers as it is for these four corporations. The value of aircraft production for the sample companies was $308,108,000 at net billing prices which, as noted above, was 75 percent of the total FOB value as given by the FAA. Therefore, by dividing the estimate for investment for the sample by this percentage as an estimate of the net additions to land, plant and equipment accomplished by all General Aviation aircraft producers during 1967, the resulting figure is $12,700,000.

The allocation of working capital made to finance additions to receivables and inventories during fiscal year 1967 is aggregated to provide another element of investment. The figures for each firm plus the total for the sample are given below. (The gross investment is assumed to be the same in 1967 as in 1966 for Lear Jet.)

Beechcraft	$ 1,832,687
Cessna	9,152,975
Piper	3,709,224
Lear Jet	503,000
Total	$15,197,886

Adjusting this figure to reflect the total gross investment related to all aircraft production, it is estimated that the gross economic impact of investment related to General Aviation aircraft production in 1967 was $20,300,000.

The $12,700,000 and $20,300,000 above relate to the aircraft producers only, and must be factored to include the investment impact of supplier industries. It is indicated that material purchases represent approximately 50 percent of the cost of sales of General Aviation production.

Assuming a comparable output-investment ratio for these supplier companies results in a total gross impact of investment related to General Aviation production of $66,000,000.

These investments are forecast to grow in proportion to gross domestic sales to $94,700,-000 in 1975 and $141,800,000 in 1980.

Investment by Dealers and Distributors

A sample approach has been used for estimating the investment by dealers and distributors. There are 33 distributors in the U. S. and Canada of a major General Aviation manufacturer who, on the average, have $500,000 invested in facilities, and there are 700 corresponding dealers[10] in these two countries with an average capital investment of $200,000. On the basis of revenue miles flown in the U. S. and Canada, it is estimated that 85 percent of these dealers and distributors are in the U. S. (i.e., 28 distributors and 595 dealers are working for the manufacturer in the U. S.). In 1967 the manufacturer accounted for about 46 percent of total aircraft produced, and the value of their sales was about 28.4 percent of total fixed-wing sales. Since a distribution network is not solely a function of volume or the value of the aircraft, it is felt that the industry estimate based on the manufacturers' sales network should be based on both of these factors. It is estimated that the dealers and distributors affiliated with the particular manufacturer comprise 40 percent of all dealers and distributors in the U. S. This gives an estimate of 70 distributors and 1,500 dealers in the U. S. in 1967. The estimated total capital investment of all distributors is 70 × $500,000 = $35 million; and the corresponding figure for all dealers is 1500 × $200,000 = $300 million. Given this estimate of the total capital stock made by dealers and distributors of $335,000,000 it is assumed that 7.5 percent of this reflected gross investment in 1967. Thus it is estimated that the indirect economic impact of investment by General Aviation aircraft dealers and distributors in the U.S.A. was $25,100,000. The growth forecast is based on a combination of the rates of growth projected in dollar and unit sales, and the values

---

[10]These dealers are not only marketing aircraft, but are in other GA related activities.

forecast are $50,000,000 for 1975 and $68,-800,000 for 1980.

Investment by Fixed Base Operators

There were approximately 5,300 active fixed based operators at the end of 1967.[11] "The National Aviation Trades Association conducted a survey of some of its members to determine the financing required. It disclosed that a 'typical' operator needed about $30,000 invested in fixed assets — hangars, shop, office buildings — and an additional $30,000 invested in equipment."[12] Based upon these figures it is estimated that the capital stock of fixed based operators is equal to 5300 $\times$ $60,000 or $318,000,000. Assuming that 10 percent of this figure is an estimate of gross investment by FBOs in 1967, a value of $31,800,000 is obtained as the indirect economic impact of this General Aviation related activity. This is forecast to increase in proportion to user costs to $69,400,000 and $115,800,000 in 1975 and 1980 respectively.

It should be noted that the investment values used above apply to the total value of facilities, whether owned or leased.

g) Government Spending on General Aviation

All government expenditures on final goods and services generate economic activity. An amount of money spent by the government on aviation is represented by the total expenditures of the FAA. It would be desirable to separate the FAA budget into two categories: the amount spent on General Aviation and the amount spent on all non-related General Aviation activity. This is a difficult task since most government expenditures are spent on total aviation and there is no manner in which one can directly determine that percentage which can be attributed directly to General Aviation.

In coping with this problem the operations portion of FAA appropriations is first considered and then the Federal Aid to Airports program is analyzed.

[11]Airport Services Management, special tabulation of mailing list information performed for SPEAS.
[12]Geuting, Joseph T., Jr., "Make Economic Gains Out of Thin Air". A statement before the Greensboro Rotary Club, July 25, 1966.

FAA Operations

An FAA study has estimated the allocation of total cost of the Federal Airway System for fiscal years 1965 and 1966.[13] The findings are as follows (in $ millions):

Item	Fiscal Year 1965	1966
Total Annual Cost	$523.2	$534.1
Civil Share:		
Air Carrier	230.7	235.2
General Aviation	145.9	149.0
Military Share	146.6	149.9

These results demonstrate that General Aviation's share of the total annual cost of the airway system was about 28 percent in fiscal years 1965 and 1966. Using this ratio an estimate as to the amount of government expenditures and operations attributable to General Aviation can be made. From the FAA, estimates on the fiscal years 1967 and 1968 FAA budget appropriations were obtained, both for the total budget and for the figures on operations. From this information it is estimated that total FAA appropriations for calendar year 1967 were $955,-615,000, of which 62.6 percent or $598,476,-000 were appropriated for operations.

Using the 28 percent estimate as the General Aviation share of the operating cost of the airway system it can be stated that $167,573,000 of this portion of the FAA budget was spent for General Aviation.

The Federal Aid to Airport Program

In the FAA Handbook it is shown that from 1947-65 under the Federal Aid to Airport Program (FAAP) $155,608,339 or 16.6 percent of the total program was allocated to General Aviation airports.[14] Similar data for the period 1947-66 shows that $175,123,837 or 17.27 percent was allocated for this purpose.[15] When the 1947-65 figure is deducted from that for 1947-66 it is determined how much was allo-

[13]FAA, User Charges for the Domestic Federal Airway System, June 1965.

[14]FAA, Statistical Handbook of Aviation, p. 14.

[15]NBAA, Business Flying: Historical Statistical Operational Information, p. 30.

cated under the FAAP to General Aviation airports in 1966. The resulting figure is $19,515,-498 which is 23.6 percent of the total for that year. Since such figures are not available for 1967 it is assumed that this percentage is unchanged from 1966 to 1967. It is interesting to note that the portion of expenditures under the FAAP is higher in 1966 in comparison to the average for the period 1947-66. Since the FAAP appropriation for 1967 was $71,000,000 it can be estimated that the total Federal Government expenditure on General Aviation airports under the FAAP was $16,800,000.

Under the Federal Aid to Airport Program federal funds are allocated on a 50-50 matching basis with sponsoring agencies—usually state and local governments. However, a national airport survey reported that:

". . . on the basis of $891.3 million total airport development as eligible to be funded by federal and local governments, the survey found that in actual performance it was a 67/33 percent split:

Financing of FAAP — Eligible Airport Development

Local funds	$492 million	56%
State funds	98 million	11%
Federal funds	301 million	33%

"The above percentages are derived from the national tabulation. On a case-to-case study, at some airports Federal assistance amounted to approximately 50 percent of the total cost of eligible project development; at others the Federal contributions do not exceed 5 percent."[16]

From this information it is estimated that a significant proportion of state and local government expenditures concern General Aviation airports. These expenditures are approximately twice what the Federal Government spends on the FAAP or $33,600,000.

It should be noted that nothing has been said about the allocation of that portion of the FAAP budget not directly attributable to General Avia-

[16]Report of the National Airport Survey 1966 through 1969. Conducted jointly by: Airport Operators Council, American Association of Airport Executives, and the National Association of State Aviation Officials, December 1965, p. 9.

tion airports, nor has there been discussed the rest of the FAA budget other than the operations and FAAP items which for fiscal year 1967 comprised 65 percent of the total. Concerning the FAAP budget, it is clear that many public airports which serve air carriers also serve General Aviation, but presently there is no related allocation of airport costs. Within the total FAA budget there are other categories of expenditures such as facilities, equipment and research and development for which there is no way to estimate a breakdown between air carriers and General Aviation. As a result of these and other factors, it is considered that the report estimates of government expenditures on General Aviation are understated to some degree.

It is clear that there are additional state and local expenditures on airports, some of which are attributable to General Aviation, but about which relevant data is not available. Many of these expenditures are imbedded in public works budgets and a substantial work effort beyond the scope of this report is required for full determination.

In concluding this section it is to be acknowledged that there are some instances of "double counting". Including landing fees and taxes (fuel and other items) and at the same time including government expenditures represents such categories of "double counting". It is clear, however, that the magnitude of this problem is far outweighed by those expenditures of the various levels of government which were not quantified.

The forecast of government expenditures to 1975 and 1980 is accomplished in proportion to the increases projected for all other inputs discussed above. These values represent a valid measure of total General Aviation activity, and it is considered that government expenditures will at least parallel the activity growth. No consideration is given to an analysis of the source of these funds, whether they be financed through general fund allocations or user charges, since this would have no effect on the total impact on GNP.

Figure 71

ECONOMIC IMPACT OF GENERAL AVIATION
1967 — 1975 — 1980
Millions of Constant Dollars

	1967	1975	1980
Value of Production			
Domestic Sales of Aircraft	$ 475.3	$1,108.5	$1,660.6
Exports of Aircraft	76.5	173.7	253.6
Avionics	45.7	106.7	159.8
Exports of Engines & Avionics	70.0	159.0	232.0
Transaction Costs of Used Aircraft Sales	22.0	54.0	86.0
User Costs	683.1	1,491.0	2,488.0
Pilot Wages & Administration Overhead	521.0	941.0	1,139.0
Value of Net Investment			
Producers	66.0	153.9	230.6
Distribution	25.1	50.0	68.8
FBO	31.8	69.4	115.8
Government Expenditures			
FAA Operations	167.6		
FAAP — Federal Funds	16.8	465.6	695.5
— State Funds	33.6		
Grand Total Economic Impact	$2,234.5	$4,772.8	$7,129.7

Source: SPEAS Analysis.

The resulting values from this projection of government expenditures are $465,600,000 for 1975 and $695,500,000 for 1980.

h) *Summary Table*

A summary table of the above discussion of the economic impact of General Aviation in the years 1967, 1975 and 1980 is included as Figure 71.

i) *Intangible Benefits*

Up to this point in the discussion of General Aviation's importance to the economy, the analysis has been exclusively measured against the National Income accounts. This has largely been done from the point of view of enumerating and tabulating the various elements of economic activity which, together, make it possible to provide the services known collectively as General Aviation. This means that no assessment of the value of the service rendered has been made. As with any service industry, which is the way one must consider the *use* of General Aviation, there is no tangible product associated with its consumption and many of the benefits arising therefrom cannot be quantified in dollars and cents in the usual way, if at all. These bene-

fits have traditionally been lumped together and called "intangibles", a phrase which succinctly describes the situation in its application to many of General Aviation's uses. These intangibles, as in the discussion of the accountable benefits to the economy, may be direct or indirect and may produce secondary, and lower level benefits as well.

One of the most important items of these intangible benefits is the time saved by business executives flying in corporate aircraft compared to the use of whatever alternative means of transportation is available (if one exists at all). This item is foremost because it can at least be thought of in terms of the normal business criteria and to an important degree because other transportation industries have attempted to evaluate their time saving value. The airlines have long employed this thinking in their marketing (both consciously and unconsciously) and it is effective because the most commonly thought of alternative to commercial flying is the automobile or bus—both of which are clearly different from the airlines.

In the case of General Aviation, however, the alternative mode of transportation, almost by definition, depends on the specific circumstance under consideration. No simple (or acceptable) generalization can be made against which an estimate of the time and cost differences can be measured. The logical answer may be any one or a combination of scheduled air carrier, private or rented automobile, intercity bus or railroad.

Development of a logical way in which to consider this intangible benefit is likewise broadened by the fact that General Aviation business flying cannot be considered as a service by itself, directly generating economic activity. This is true because whatever the value added created is in business usage of General Aviation, it is recorded in the National Income Accounts as a component of the value added in the individual industries which employ General Aviation flying. What can be said, as with investment expenditures, is that this is an indirect contribution of General Aviation. In this case again, the industry's services are being used as inputs in other industries in order to produce their own higher value.

In 1962, a study was conducted in which an attempt was made to evaluate the benefits of aviation as measured by its impact on the U. S. economy, somewhat as has been done in this study.[17] This was not the primary objective of the 1962 study, but the authors did approximate the value of the primary intangible of time saved through business flying. In that study it was estimated that the total value of the time savings accruing to users of corporate aircraft was $550.7 million (as measured in dollars per executive hour saved) and that the added cost of the corporate aircraft use amounted to $418.2 million for 1960. The net value of the time saved, therefore, amounted to $132.5 million, which could be considered as having an impact on the economy as an *indirect* result of General Aviation.

Using a similar approach (but updating both data and assumptions with regard to the alternative mode), it is possible to produce a like figure for 1967.

[17]United Research Inc., "Economic Criteria for Federal Aviation Agency Expenditures", 1962.

SPEAS estimates that 8,483,000 hours were flown for business reasons, including the FAA's category called executive transportation. Assuming occupancy of approximately 4 passengers,[18] apart from professional pilots and others not actively related to the conduct of the business for which the flying was done, this would produce 33.9 million passenger-hours.

If these passenger-hours had been undertaken by private automobile, this would have produced roughly 162.9 million passenger hours.[19] This is a valid, practical assumption for many of the business flying circumstances because of the relatively short distance normally involved and the often inconvenience or total lack of comparable scheduled airline service. From this estimate it can be seen that the net time saving between the two alternatives is 129.0 million passenger-hours (162.9 − 33.9). These hours can be assumed to have a value at least equal to that of businessmen using commercial airlines, if not higher, so that the gross value of these hours saved is approximately $1,290 million (using a $20,000 average salary and a 2,000 productive hour executive year).

However, since the cost of flying is greater than that of automobile travel, the net savings are lower. Based on an average cost per plane hour of $36.00,[20] and an average of 4 passengers, the cost per passenger hour of corporate aircraft is $9.00. If the average automobile cost of $1.30 per passenger hour is subtracted from that for air,[21] a net unit difference of $7.70 is obtained. This is the additional cost per business passenger hour of flying business aircraft. Multiplying this by the business hours saved:

[18]SPEAS survey—Reference discussion of passengers in General Aviation flying.

[19]This assumes a circuity of 20% for highway travel and a ratio of aircraft to automobile speeds of 4 to 1, including trip times to and from airports for air travel.

[20]Weighted average of cost per hour for executive types of aircraft from SPEAS analysis, including paid pilot costs where appropriate.

[21]The American Automobile Association variously reports out-of-pocket operating expenses for automobiles at between 3.2 and 5.7 cents depending on geographic area and operating conditions. Assuming a midway figure of 5 cents, an average speed of 50 miles per hour and occupancy of 2.0, the cost per passenger hour is roughly $1.30.

$129 million $\times$ $7.70 = 993 million. Therefore, the added net production in the economy resulting from business use of General Aviation in 1967 was the value of the time saved less the added cost of providing those hours, or $1290 million — $993 million = $297 million. This compares generally with the $132.5 million estimated for 1960. The comparison — included to give some measure of the magnitude of the unrefined numbers — is not strictly valid since many of the assumptions used for the 1960 estimate are no longer valid.[22] The general conclusion which is valid is that the net benefit from business use of General Aviation is growing at a rapid rate; more rapidly than the overall economy so that its relative importance is increasing.

Without question this finding is merely an "order of magnitude" estimate and is in no way definitive, nor should it be. In the context of this analysis of intangibles, there are so many areas within business flying which defy quantification, that it makes little sense to be precise in this one item which does provide some basis for logical application of valuation.

Neither of these analyses encompasses the many other intangible benefits being realized from business use of General Aviation. Each of the alternative modes open to the businessman is usually less desirable from the point of view of business productivity, apart from the study of time saving. Such consideration must cope with many un-analyzable circumstances including:

- The value of earlier decisions and action made possible by the use of business General Aviation flying.
- The value of less fatigue arising from the use of corporate aircraft.
- The value of greater usefulness of trained, experienced executives.
- The value of decentralized production made possible through efficient communications between headquarters and plants.
- The value of being able to expand market areas through more effective use of management and sales executives.

[22]Such as using rail travel as the substitute for General Aviation flying in 1960.

It may be, if there were a way to quantify these items, that the total benefit to the economy arising from business use of corporate aircraft would be double the executive time saving value (a conservative estimate) considering the potential importance of each of the above items. This would produce an approximate total value of intangible benefits of $600 million for the year 1967 for business flying.

Regarding personal flying, the most obvious intangible is the value of recreational time to those pursuing personal flying for other than business reasons. This is a benefit to the economy in several diverse, yet still intangible, ways. The range extends from being able to "get away from it all" to education through travel. The major problem in measuring the benefit is that "the relationship between price (cost) and total relevant benefit is drastically uneven for different sorts of recreation for different sorts of people, having different amounts and kinds of leisure time and education".[23]

Apart from the truth of this statement, it is possible to make a gross estimate of the possible intangible value of recreational flying. The Outdoor Recreation Resources Review Committee and others have surveyed families to determine the value of their recreational time. In most cases and certainly for the average, very little monetary value is placed on such time (an average of about 30 cents per person per hour).

Since the average private General Aviation airplane owner is better than twice as well off as the average U. S. citizen, some judgment can be made about the minimum value of his recreational time.[24] Even if it is assumed that the recreational flyer's incremental income merely allows him to own/rent and operate a private plane, and his resulting valuation of the recreational time remains at 30 cents per hour, the total value of the recreational time approaches $7 million.[25] This assumes that all hours flown

[23]R. P. Mack & S. Myers, *Outdoor Recreation,* The Brookings Institution, Nov. 1963.
[24]Confidential market surveys conducted by a major manufacturer.
[25]Based on personal flying hours of 5,470,000 in 1967 with an average occupancy of 3 together with instructional flying of 5,916,000 hours and 1 passenger, or 22,326,000 passenger hours total.

for personal reasons were for recreational purposes which, of course, they were not. However, the other major use of personal flying, personal emergency or business travel, should logically have a higher intangible value to the flyer than normal recreation. If anything, then, the conservatism inherent in the above assumption yields what is probably a minimum intangible value of personal flying.

Another factoring process which has some validity in logic, if not in fact, is that of comparing learning costs. For example, it is reasonable to say that learning to drive is motivated largely by recreational impulses and may indicate the value level of recreation to the average U. S. citizen. Similarly, if the learning costs of flying indicate the level for private plane users, and the approximate ratio of these costs is 1 to 10, then it is possible to say that, apart from operating and owning costs, the private flyer values his recreational flying time at $3.00 per hour. This figure would produce a total intangible value for 1967 of $67 million. This would appear to be a more reasonable answer than the $7 million, especially if one takes the position that the intangible value of personal flying is a marginal increment over the cost of operating the aircraft, say 20 percent.

There are no data available with which an estimate of the true marginal value can be made. Nonetheless, if the 20 percent is approximately accurate for all personal flying, then the estimate of $67 million takes on added credibility: $.20 \times \$14.50 \times 22.3M$ hours $= \$64.7$ million. The true value, if it is ever possible to determine it more precisely, may well lie between the extremes computed herein. Suffice it to say that the order of magnitude of recreational, personal business and other personal reasons for flying lies in the less than $100 million range.

In terms of intangible benefits to the economy, estimating those associated with the utility flying category is virtually impossible except in a case by case study of each of the specific applications of General Aviation aircraft. In most cases, however, it is reasonable to conclude that the intangible values of this type of flying are subsumed directly in the value of the operating costs, since there are often no alternative ways of providing the service rendered.

Upon considering the many intangible ways General Aviation has an impact on the nation's economy, it is SPEAS's finding that quantifying even a very few of the most important items is reduced to judgment because of the very diversity which named the industry. It would require a singular research effort of considerably greater proportions than the present one to begin to accomplish the task. SPEAS was asked by GAMA to consider the intangible items of benefit and to make preliminary judgments wherever data permitted. To that end, the objective has been met and, upon the findings of this analysis, it is questionable whether further research is warranted and/or would be fruitful. In most cases it is probably sufficient to estimate that the total value of the intangibles associated with General Aviation is between $700 million and $1,000 million, or about 50% of the tangible benefits.

Although not in the terms used in the preceding analysis of the over-all economic impact measurement, it is useful to consider the many items of intangible benefits which accrue to the economy from General Aviation use. Used with some imagination and knowledge of the industry, the following outline suggests the many ways in which General Aviation has a beneficial, if intangible and unmeasurable, impact on the economy. Most if not all in the final analysis, cannot be specified in monetary terms, notwithstanding the fact that many of their components stem from economic factors:

1. Value of time saved (by passenger plus "domino effect") —
    a) Business flying.
    b) Pleasure flying.
    c) Utility flying.
2. Emergency value (human life and property) —
    a) Natural disaster (earthquakes, floods, wind, weather).
    b) Crime control and law enforcement.
    c) Riots and civil disturbance.
    d) Rescue and life saving.

e) Forest fire fighting.

f) Business decisions.

g) Food drops for animals and other forms of remote resupply.

h) Ambulance service.

i) Industry equipment and repairs.

3. National defense value —

a) Pilot training and availability.

b) Saving in military aircraft through joint sharing of aircraft development and production costs.

c) Value to war time combat use.

d) Civil Air Patrol.

e) Efficient and productive plant operations during war time.

4. Promotion or stimulation of air carrier flying (ticket sales) —

5. Entertainment value —

a) Value to General Aviation passengers (in terms of gratification):

1) Air shows.

2) Radio, TV, movies.

3) Vacation and resort area development.

4) Sightseeing and other transportation modes.

b) Value to entertainment industry:

Prorata portion of entertainment industry facilities, equipment, labor expense, operating costs (fuel, electricity, etc.), taxes, interest for vacation and resort areas and sightseeing and other elements of the entertainment industry.

6. General business industry associated with General Aviation Travel —

Prorata portion of general business activity resulting from General Aviation passenger travel including facilities, equipment, labor expense, operating costs, taxes, interest for such elements as:

1) Hotels.

2) Ground transportation (taxi, limousine, car rental, etc.).

3) Air carrier helicopter services.

4) Meals.

7. Specific benefits related to General Aviation —

a) Aerial photography and mapping.

b) Fish spotting and fish saving.

c) Forest fire patrol.

d) Power and pipe line patrol.

e) Corporation internal business aircraft management, maintenance and operations, personnel and expenses.

8. Related business development —

a) Development of industry near General Aviation airports (factories and plants).

b) Development of geographically isolated areas (mining, oil, timber).

9. Incentive to foreign businesses who then emulate, interact with and stimulate U. S. businesses, including their second-order effect in generating facilities and services.

10. National prestige (growing fleets of aircraft in under-developed countries).

11. Social cohesion and unity through increased avenues of personal contact and communication.

12. Political benefits derived from the positive influences of relative stability and growth in income and employment, and foreign trade impact.

j) *Micro-Economic Analysis of the General Aviation Aircraft Production*

This discussion is included as an addendum to the findings reported above concerning the value to the economy of General Aviation aircraft production. The results of this theoretical approach generally confirm the practical and pragmatic approach to the measurement of economic impact adopted throughout this study.

From micro-economic theory it is known that the level of output of an industry is determined by the supply and demand conditions pertaining to that industry. An analytical study or prediction of output and prices of an industry must then include the quantification of these schedules, as was done above. For most purposes, however, it is not enough for decision-makers to understand why and how the industry's production has grown. They also require some knowledge as to the expansion of plant and employment necessary to support future expected growth in their sector. This latter part involves a third relationship between capital and labor and their interaction given the technological conditions. The questions which must be considered are, in the following order:

What are the factors that affect the demand for General Aviation output? From this relationship, what can be said about the future demand?

Given these demand estimates, and assuming market clearance, what is the relationship between capital and labor of the industry, that the production conditions in that industry imply?

What will the absolute levels of capital and labor be, given the results of production analysis and looking at the supply of factors determined by their relative scarcity in the entire economy?

Before considering each of these problems in detail, it is useful to clarify a few definitions and explain certain data characteristics.

The simplest approach to defining the output of General Aviation aircraft activity is to count the physical number of planes it produces and sells. However, there are two problems which are associated with this procedure. First of all, the products of various firms that comprise the industry are not homogeneous. If a small piston engine aircraft is counted as one unit of output, a jet which employs relatively more resources, should be weighted more heavily. For example, assume that last year the industry produced three piston engine executive transports; and this year, two such aircraft and a jet. In this hypothetical example, the output remains unchanged if we take the physical count, as in the former method. But while the piston plane costs approximately $150,000, a small jet is worth around $750,000. This year's physical output, therefore, is not three but five. Technically, this amounts to weighting the quantities produced by various concerns by their prices relative to the value of one commodity called the numeraire:

$$\sum_i \frac{P_i}{P_o} q_i = \bar{q}$$

P_i = prices
q_i = quantities
$_i$ = type of aircraft

The choice of the numeraire, P_o, is arbitrary and does not affect the computations. In 1967

the average price of all types of aircraft was $25,639 and for this discussion is set as P_o:

$$\sum \left(\frac{q_i}{\Sigma q_i}\right) P_i = P_o$$

The weighted sum of various types of aircraft for that same year was 12,017, equal to the unit count. To disperse the apparent paradox, it should be emphasized that this happens because the average price was chosen as the numeraire.

In order to adjust the output figures of periods preceding 1967, it is not sufficient to repeat the above weighting process. Because year to year prices of a given type of plane will vary reflecting the general economic fluctuations. Expanding the simplistic case, assume that there is only one type of plane being produced. In 1967 there were, for example, 5,000 planes each costing $25,000; and in 1966 these figures were respectively 4,000 and $24,000. According to the weighting procedure proposed, the adjusted quantity figure for the 1966 output would be given by:

$$\frac{24,000}{25,000} \times 4,000 = 3,840$$

which is not the true figure. The change in the numeraire's price, which stems from general inflationary or deflationary tendencies should be then explicitly accounted for.

In view of these considerations the heterogeneous physical output figures from 1958 through 1967 were adjusted as follows:

First, the 1967 average price of General Aviation aircraft was calculated as the ratio of the value of planes produced to their number.

Then using the consumer price index time series from 1958-1967, the price of a typical plane was calculated.

Finally, the value of aircraft produced was divided by this deflated price index of a typical plane and the time series of "adjusted physical output" obtained.

Although the statistics on physical output and value of this output are readily available, it is difficult to collect series on capital and labor for the entire industry. Consequently, in estimating the model, a sample composed of four companies was used accounting for better than 75 percent of the industry's total output.

The employment figures used are "number of employees". It would have been perhaps more precise to use the number of manhours which is a better indicator of labor input.

The capital series used in estimating the production function is the net value of land, plant, and equipment. Both the capital and labor data for the four companies were obtained from their annual reports.

The Demand

A demand schedule expresses physical output as a function of the good's own price. The implicit assumption to this simple relationship is that the income and the prices of other goods are constant. Although this may be the case in the short run, over the long run such a simplification is not realistic. Prices of other goods, and incomes do change and cause shifts in the price-quantity schedule. Hence, two more variables must be added to the demand equation: Gross National Product and consumer price index. Formally, the demand function has the formulation:

$$q = a_o Y^{a1} I^{a2}$$

where
q = quantity demanded
Y = GNP
I = consumer price index

It will be recalled that in the adjustment of the physical output it was assumed that the prices of General Aviation aircraft change in the same manner as the consumer price index. Hence, it can be shown mathematically that the exponential of I, a_2, is the sum of its own price elasticity and the cross-elasticities with respect to all other goods. On theoretical grounds, it is expected *a priori* that a_2 be a negative value. Again, the exponential a_1 is the income elasticity of output; and since aircraft are technically luxury goods, a value for a_2 should be obtained which is larger than unity. The estimated values for a_1 and a_2 should also conform to one more theoretical constraint. If from one year to the next all the prices and incomes double, the quantity demanded would not change. In terms

of the above demand equation this means that the sum of a_1 and a_2 must equal zero.

The Production Function

The production function estimated is of the Cobb-Douglas type. It expresses output produced as a function of labor and capital. Specifically:

$$q = \beta_o K^1 L^2$$
K = capital
L = labor

It is a well known fact that if β_1 and β_2 add up to unity this means that industry has constant returns to scale. If this sum is greater than one, the result is increasing returns to scale, meaning that a proportionate increase in labor and capital inputs will raise output more than proportionately. That is, if capital and labor double, the output will more than double. The General Aviation aircraft production process has not, in all probability, realized all of its potential economies (internal and external), and the latter is the case.

The Expansion Path

Expansion path is a functional relationship between capital and labor, given the production function and the prices of primary factors. The crucial assumption it embodies is that the firms are profit maximizers. If total revenue is pq and total cost, $rK + wL$ where price p; return on capital, r; and wages, w; are fixed according to the general economic conditions; the profits are equal to:

$$\pi = pq - rK - wL$$

The expansion path is derived from the first order conditions for maximization of this expression.[26] In general, this function may be written as:

$$K = \delta_o L^{\delta 1}$$

The Estimation of the Model

Imposing on these three equations (the demand function, the production relationship and the expansion path) the condition that the market

[26]For a thorough discussion of this subject, see Henderson and Quandt, *Microeconomic Theory*, McGraw Hill, New York, 1958.

is always in equilibrium, meaning supply is always equal to demand, a quantitive model of the General Aviation aircraft production industry is obtained which is fully justified by theoretical considerations. Furthermore, it can be shown that the parameters of this system of simultaneous equations are estimable. Because of some technical properties of these equations (all three functions are over-identified), the ordinary multi-variate regression analysis cannot be used. From among the suitable methods available, the two-stage least squares method has been adopted.

Results

The estimate of the demand equation for the four companies in the sample is:

$$q = 195.5 \ Y^{2.91} \ I^{-3.23}$$

Various statistical tests based on earlier theoretical hypotheses were confirmed by the calculations. For instance, one can empirically assert that the exponentials of income and price index sum up to zero (the asymptotic chi square (χ^2) for this test was .004). The signs of 2.91 and -3.23 are also in conformity with normal expectations. Overall goodness of fit of this equation given by an asymptotic value of 32,700 shows that the demand equation is a close representation of the real world.

The same positive results hold for the estimated supply equation which was:

$$q = 42.8 \ K^{.72} \ L^{.89}$$

The asymptotic χ^2 for its goodness of fit was in the order of 53,500; even better than demand equation's χ^2. Also the chi-square for the homogeneity assumption was greater than 11; with the implication that the industry operates under increasing returns to sale.

The expansion path function was:

$$K = 4.3 \ L^{.78}$$

With its goodness of fit meaure $\chi^2 = 8,500$.

The preceding are interesting from the point of view of defining what has already occurred. The second objective of this analysis is to predict future output, capital and labor of the industry. Given these quantitative relationships

what can be said about the uncertain future outcomes? The first thing to note is that the equations were obtained from a sample of four firms. Although it is probably safe to assume that the technical conditions of production and the capital-labor relationship are identical for the entire industry, the demand function expresses only a portion of the total market for General Aviation aircraft. However, the share of four companies in the sample between 1958 and 1967 was about 75 percent of the total industry, with only slight deviations from this mean. This finding was used to estimate the total for 1967 and to point-predict the total output, capital and labor for the years of 1975 and 1980 in the following manner.

Using current GNP estimates of the McGraw-Hill Economics Department and assuming a 2.5 percent inflation per year, the estimated demand for the sample companies for the forecast years was considered. These figures are presented in line 1 of the following Figure 72.

The total demand of the industry, line 2, was obtained by simply multiplying line 1 with the scalar 1.3333, expecting that during the coming years the four companies will continue to hold 75 percent of the market (an assumption which may prove conservative if the opinions of these companies are correct).

Finally, substituting the total output figures produced by the model into the production function, and utilizing also the expansion path equation, the total capital and labor requirements were projected for the industry as presented in line 3 and line 4 respectively.

Line 5 gives predictions of the value of the output, on the earlier assumption that the average price of fixed-wing aircraft will vary as the general prices, namely at the rate of 2.5 percent per year.

The last line recounts SPEAS' previously arrived at forecast of General Aviation production (domestic sales) for comparison and confirmation purposes.

To reiterate, the output figures are a weighted sum of various types of fixed-wing aircraft; as such they are different from a simple count of

Figure 72

ESTIMATED VALUE OF PRODUCTION OF GENERAL AVIATION AIRCRAFT THROUGH MICRO-ECONOMIC ANALYSIS

	1967	1975	1980
(1) Adjusted Demand For Manufacturers Included In The Sample (G/A Aircraft Units)	11,650	19,340	24,590
(2) Total Adjusted Demand (G/A Aircraft Units)	15,533	25,787	32,787
(3) Capital (In Thousands)	$57.88	$76.02	$86.50
(4) Labor (Employees)	27,730	39,250	46,270
(5) Value of Micro-Economic Model (In Millions)	$398[1]	$936	$1,348
(6) Production (Output) Empirical Projection (In Millions)	$475	$1,086	$1,629

[1]This corresponds to the $475.3 million value of production discussed in the preceding section of this report. The value estimated by the model is the result of averaging over the 10-year data history used in this analysis, which discounts the unusually active years of 1965-1967.

Source: SPEAS Analysis.

Figure 73

ADJUSTED OUTPUT AND OTHER PARAMETER VALUES REQUIRED IN THE MODEL

Year	Adjusted Output for the Sample	GNP in Current Billion Dollars	Consumer Price Index	Land, Plant And Equipment For the Sample in Million Dollars	Labor for the Sample
1958	4,078	$447.3	100.7	$26.218	13,232
1959	5,119	483.7	101.5	29.360	15,172
1960	5,932	503.7	103.1	32.674	13,833
1961	4,712	520.1	104.2	33.822	11,196
1962	5,151	560.3	105.4	34.504	12,429
1963	5,646	590.5	106.7	36.043	13,638
1964	7,395	632.4	108.1	37.200	16,557
1965	11,402	683.9	109.9	42.525	18,722
1966	13,428	743.3	113.1	51.067	23,855
1967	12,017	785.1	116.3	60.566	25,340

Source: SPEAS Analysis.

physical units. Value of the total output is calculated at net billing price and not retail value.

The data used in the estimation of the equations presented in the preceding figure, for the year 1967, fall somewhat below the observed value (See Figure 73). For instance, while actual number of planes for the sample was 12,017, the model estimated it to be 11,650. Similarly, while $58 million was the value of land, plant and equipment for the total industry in Figure 72, the actual number for the four sample firms alone was $60 million. Looking closely at the actual data, however, shows that the last three years are considerably higher than the ones for previous years as noted elsewhere in this report. Also, there is a drop in output from 1966 to 1967. There are two possible interpretations of these phenomena. Either there has been structural change in the industry during the years 1965-67, in which case the model underestimated the future output, capital and labor. Or, as the downturn from 1966 to 1967 might indicate, during the last three years the industry has enjoyed an unusual boom, and will return to the basic relationships described by the model. The similarity of the results obtained from the two entirely different approaches confirms the validity of the method adopted for this report (the empirical projection) and the results thereof. In addition, however, it is possible through the above model to gain projections of the capital and labor requirements for the future which, as described in the opening paragraphs of this section of the report, are highly important for industry planners.

APPENDIX

The following pages contain the equations used
to forecast the demand for aircraft by state developed in Chapter 2.

STATES EQUATION
WEST SOUTH CENTRAL REGION
OKLAHOMA, TEXAS, ARKANSAS, LOUISIANA

Variables:

X_1 = % of families with income greater than or equal to $10,000.

X_2 = Auto sales.

X_3 = Number of Airports.

Equation:

$$Y = -871.94 + 4.93X_1 + 1.04X_2 + 16.60X_3$$

Standard Deviations of Coefficients	T-Ratio	Beta Coefficients
1.42	3.4	.06
.16	6.3	.40
1.72	9.6	.56

Standard error of estimate = 184

Coefficient of Multiple Correlation = .998

F level = 1894

Degrees of Freedom = (3,24)

Durbin-Watson = 1.63

STATES EQUATION
WEST NORTH CENTRAL REGION
KANSAS, MISSOURI, NEBRASKA, NORTH DAKOTA, SOUTH DAKOTA, MINNESOTA, IOWA

Variables:

X_1 = Number of families with income greater than or equal to $10,000.

X_2 = Per household auto sales.

X_3 = Number of large cities population greater than or equal to 100,000 in the state.

X_4 = Number of airports.

X_5 = Qualitative variable = 1 for South Dakota and North Dakota and zero elsewhere.

Equation:

$$Y = -1163.15 + .0019X_1 + 1174.62X_2 + 421.95X_3 + 12.03X_4 + 397.0X_5$$

Standard Deviations of Coefficients	T-Ratio	Beta Coefficients
.0006	3.39	.21
233.20	5.03	.19
30.31	13.91	.70
2.11	5.69	.37
66.58	5.96	.27

Standard error of estimate = 170

Coefficient of Multiple Correlation = .974

F level = 157

Degrees of Freedom = (5,43)

Durbin-Watson = 1.10

STATES EQUATION
EAST NORTH CENTRAL REGION
ILLINOIS, INDIANA, MICHIGAN, OHIO, WISCONSIN

Variables:

X_1 = Auto sales.

X_2 = Number of households.

Equation:

$$Y = 654.67 + .80X_1 + .425X_2$$

Standard Deviations of Coefficients	T-Ratio	Beta Coefficients
.1007	7.9	.65
.1020	4.1	.34

Standard error of estimate = 252

Coefficient of Multiple Correlation = .971

F level = 263

Degrees of Freedom = (2,32)

Durbin-Watson = 1.51

STATES EQUATION
MOUNTAIN REGION
UTAH, MONTANA, IDAHO, COLORADO, WYOMING, NEW MEXICO, NEVADA, ARIZONA

Variables:

X_1 = Auto sales per household.

X_2 = Number of large cities, population greater than or equal to 100,000, in state.

X_3 = Number of airports.

$X_4 - X_6$ = Qualitative variables to reflect particular characteristics of some states.

X_4 = 1 for Utah, zero otherwise.

X_5 = 1 for Wyoming, zero otherwise.

X_6 = 1 for Idaho, Colorado, Montana, zero otherwise.

Equation:

$$Y = 364.77 + 853.59X_1 + 361.91X_2 + 6.55X_3 - 425.77X_4 - 154.42X_5 + 224.48X_6$$

Standard Deviations of Coefficients	T-Ratio	Beta Coefficients
196.09	4.3	.23
46.42	7.7	.68
3.60	1.82	.20
63.47	-6.7	-.38
73.45	-2.1	-.13
96.40	2.3	.29

Standard error of estimate = 144

Coefficient of Multiple Correlation = .93

F level = 52

Degrees of Freedom = (6,49)

Durbin-Watson = 1.62

STATES EQUATION
NEW ENGLAND REGION
CONNECTICUT, MAINE, MASSACHUSETTS, NEW HAMPSHIRE, RHODE ISLAND, VERMONT

Variables:

X_1 = Auto sales.

X_2 = Number of airports.

Equation:

$$Y = -21.09 + .77X_1 + 7.38X_2$$

Standard Deviations of Coefficients	T-Ratio	Beta Coefficients
.038	20.3	.78
1.15	6.4	.24

Standard error of estimate = 63

Coefficient of Multiple Correlation = .988

F level = 773

Degrees of Freedom = (2,39)

Durbin-Watson = 1.226

STATES EQUATION
PACIFIC REGION
ALASKA, CALIFORNIA, WASHINGTON, OREGON

Variables:

X_1 = Auto sales.

X_2 = Number of airports.

Equation:

$$Y = -1276.65 + .64X_1 + 45.27X_2$$

Standard Deviations of Coefficients	T-Ratio	Beta Coefficients
.13	4.7	.29
3.98	11.3	.71

Standard error of estimate = 759

Coefficient of Multiple Correlation = .988

F level = 505

Degrees of Freedom = (2,25)

Durbin-Watson = 1.449

STATES EQUATION
MID ATLANTIC REGION
NEW JERSEY, NEW YORK, PENNSYLVANIA

Variables:

X_1 = Number of families with income greater than or equal to $10,000.

X_2 = Auto sales per household.

X_3 = Number of airports.

Equation:

$$Y = -948.65 + .0014X_1 + 1763.34X_2 + 14.82X_3$$

Standard Deviations of Coefficients	T-Ratio	Beta Coefficients
.0002	8.7	.71
509.78	3.4	.26
2.32	6.3	.50

Standard error of estimate = 266

Coefficient of Multiple Correlation = .959

F level = 64

Degrees of Freedom = (3,17)

Durbin-Watson = 1.37

STATES EQUATION
SOUTH ATLANTIC REGION (1)
DELAWARE, WEST VIRGINIA, D.C.

Variable:

X_1 = Number of families with income greater than or equal to $10,000.

Equation:

$$Y = 189.55 + .0039X_1$$

Standard Deviation of Coefficient	T-Ratio	Beta Coefficient
.0009	4.51	.71

Standard error of estimate = 78

Coefficient of Multiple Correlation = .72

F level = 20

Degrees of Freedom = (1,19)

Durbin-Watson = 2.02

STATES EQUATION
SOUTH ATLANTIC REGION (2)
MARYLAND, NORTH CAROLINA, SOUTH CAROLINA, GEORGIA, FLORIDA, VIRGINIA

Variables:

X_1 = Number of households with income greater than or equal to $10,000.

X_2 = Auto sales per household.

X_3 = Number of airports.

Equation:

$$Y = -1843.33 + .0024X_1 + 1185.36X_2 + 3286X_3$$

Standard Deviations of Coefficients	T-Ratio	Beta Coefficients
.0009	2.76	.199
457.08	2.59	.197
2.40	13.65	.760

Standard error of estimate = 312

Coefficient of Multiple Correlation = .949

F level = 115

Degrees of Freedom = (3,38)

Durbin-Watson = 1.28

STATES EQUATION
EAST SOUTH CENTRAL REGION
ALABAMA, MISSISSIPPI, KENTUCKY, TENNESSEE

Variables:

X_1 = % of families with income greater than or equal to $10,000.

X_2 = Number of airports.

Equation:

$$Y = 93.4 + 4.17X_1 + 7.45X_2$$

Standard Deviations of Coefficients	T-Ratio	Beta Coefficients
.92	4.5	.57
1.7	4.2	.53

Standard error of estimate = 171

Coefficient of Multiple Correlation = .774

F level = 18

Degrees of Freedom = (2,25)

Durbin-Watson = 1.128

STATES EQUATION
HAWAII

Variable:

X_1 = Number of households with income greater than or equal to $10,000.

Equation:

$$Y = 10.19 + .0025X_1$$

Standard Deviation of Coefficient	T-Ratio	Beta Coefficient
.0005	5.6	.93

Standard error of estimate = 14

Coefficient of Multiple Correlation = .93

F level = 31

Degrees of Freedom = (1,5)

Durbin-Watson = 2.14

DATA SOURCES

The following list of sources and documents is intended solely to identify some of the more important sources of information used in the preparation of this study. It does not pretend to be exhaustive, or to provide data sources for General Aviation outside the United States.

Books and Reports

Arizona State University. *A Study to Determine the Feasibility of Establishing a National Program for Training Skilled Aviation Personnel.* July, 1967.

Council of Economic Advisors. *Economic Report of the President.* February, 1968.

Fromm, Gary. *Measuring Benefits of Government Investments.* The Brookings Institution. April, 1965.

Little, Arthur D. Inc. *A Survey of the Executive Aircraft Market.* June, 1965.

McGraw-Hill, Economics Department. *The American Economy — Prospects for Growth Through 1982.* 1968.

Sales Management. *Survey of Buying Power.* Bill Publications. Annual Editions.

Time Magazine. *The Men Who Buy New Private Airplanes. Research Report 1302.* 1964.

_____*New Pilots. A Survey of the Individuals Obtaining Pilots' Licenses in 1963. Research Report 1301.* 1964.

Transportation Workshop. *Air Transportation 1975 and Beyond: a Systems Approach; Report.* Co-chairmen: Bernard A. Schriever and William W. Seifert. M.I.T. Press. 1968.

Government Documents

Federal Aviation Administration

_____*Airport Master Records (Form 5010-1, superseding Form 29A).* Annual Editions.

_____*Air Traffic Activity.* Annual Editions.

_____*Aircraft Registration Master File Magnetic Tapes,* as of February 29, 1968, March 31, 1968, March 31, 1969.

_____*The Airport — Its Influence on the Community Economy.* 1967.

_____*Aviation Forecasts for Years 1968-1979.* January 1968.

_____*Aviation Forecasts for Years 1967-1977.* January 1967.

_____*Aviation Forecasts for Years 1966-1971.* December 1965.

_____*Aviation Forecasts for Years 1963-1968.* November 1962.

_____*Census of U.S. Civil Aircraft.* Annual Editions.

_____*Forecasts of Air Traffic Activity CONUS 1965-1980.* July 1965.

_____*General Aviation Aircraft Owners Survey.* 1962.

_____*General Aviation: A Study and Forecast of the Fleet and Its Use in 1975.* July 1966.

_____*Scheduled Air Taxi Operators,* as of October 1967, November 1966, November, 1965.

_____*Statistical Handbook of Aviation.* Annual Editions.

Industrial and Trade Associations

Aerospace Industries Association of America Inc.

_____*Aerospace Facts and Figures.* 1955-1968.

_____*Exports of Utility Aircraft, by Model and Value.* 1957-1967.

_____*General Aviation Airplane Shipments.* 1964-1968.

_____*Shipments of Civil Aircraft.* 1947-1963.
Aircraft Owners and Pilots Association

_____*General Aviation Aircraft Specifications.* 1966.

_____*Profile of Flying and Buying.* Annual Editions.
Aircraft Dealers Service Association

_____*Aircraft Bluebook.* January 1968.
National Business Aircraft Association

_____*Business Flying, Special Reports.* February 1964, March 1967, April 1968.

In addition to the material cited above, reference was made to aircraft manufacturers' annual reports, proprietary market studies, state aeronautical data and the aeronautical press.